Everything for the RoadMaker

Illustrated History - 1875 to 1945

By William Barlow

and

Rhea Hamilton Seeger

Editor

Published by
POSSIBILITIES

Published by
POSSIBILITIES
Rural Route 3, Auburn,
Ontario, Canada NOM IEO

Canadian Cataloguing in Publication Data
Barlow, William, 1918–
Everything for the roadmaker

ISBN 0-9695643-0-9

1. Roads – Canada – Design and construction – History. 2. Road
construction industry – Canada – History. 3. Road construction
equipment industry – Canada – History. 4. Dominion Road Machinery
Company. I. Seeger, Rhea Hamilton, 1954–. II. Title.

HD9717.5.R.6B37 1991   388.1'0971 C91-095536-0

Select halftones and line shots by
Rising Graphics

Printed by Beacon Herald Fine Printing
Stratford, Ontario, Canada

Cover photo courtesy of the Ministry of Transportation
Cover design by Bill Barlow Jr.

Contents

Preface

As a mobile population, we expect well-constructed and maintained roads to ease the ever-growing burden of traffic and reduce our travelling time on the highways.

However, the super highways and 'black-top' of today are relatively new and we have to go back only two generations when gravel or 'macadamized' roads were the prevailing types of highway surfaces both in town and in the country. Before that, travellers had to contend with semi-maintained dirt trails and the occasional stretch of plank road or corduroy road.

This book fills the literary gap, dealing with the history of road making and maintenance equipment, and with the methods of road construction in North America from 1875 to 1945. I have also told the story of one of the principal, pioneering manufacturers of road making equipment. This company, known today as Champion Road Machinery Limited and based in Goderich, Ontario, has had a tumultuous history. What was just a patchwork of verbal and written accounts has now been accurately published in its entirety.

Between these covers you will find fascinating information about the ingenuity needed to construct roads properly, a photographic record of the men and machines, and how one company specialized in "everything for the road maker".

While researching and writing this book, I have been indebted to many people and organizations, as shown in the list of acknowledgements in the back. I would be remiss, however, if I didn't express my deepest gratitude to Rhea Hamilton-Seeger for her perseverance as editor, typist, and advisor.

Last but not least, I dedicate this book to my father-in-law, Harry T. Barker, an extraordinary man who spent almost sixty years with the American Road Machine Company of Canada, Limited and The Dominion Road Machinery Company Limited and to the many employees who believed in the future of better machines for the making of better roads.

William Barlow

The creation of a road

The first roads through the wilderness were products of man's strength. The roads taken for granted today are products of man's ingenuity. As a variety of methods were developed and abandoned in the development of durable roads, designs for equipment that would alleviate the work were being invented.

To appreciate the thought and necessity of road building and machinery development one has to review the history of road making and meet the men who pursued the future down the roads of yesterday.

The fur trade, while dependent on the Canadian Shield for a supply of furs also relied on the development of agriculture at convenient intervals to support the heavy cost of transportation. The government was well aware of this dependence. Prosperity for the new country hinged on settlement, and that could be increased with the development of a road system through the new lands.

The government's Colonization Roads program focused on building major north-south and east-west trunk roads to link the settled portion of Ontario to the frontier. Land parcels of no more than 100 acres located along the surveyed routes were granted to settlers. Progress was limited, for it was a mammoth task for each man and his family to clear and build a passable road. Each settler worked the section of road that faced his property. The road developed further, if and when, the next adjacent settler moved in.

Some main arteries into the interior of Ontario were initiated by the militia, which had a mandate to open a route to the Upper Lakes of Simcoe. But this progress was soon curtailed when in 1794 the threat of an American invasion drew the troops away to the Niagara border. While the Surveyor General, a government office, surveyed the main routes, it was companies such as the Canadian Land and Emigration Company, the German Land Company, and the Canada Company and large local landowners such as Colonel Talbot in the London area, that were instrumental in the opening up of large tracts of land.

There were standards for roads set by surveyors and professional road builders. One such man, Asa Danforth, accepted a contract to build a road from Kingston to York.

The terms of contract called for a 33-foot side road with the

The early dirt roads were severely affected by rain and narrow wheel rims which created ruts that held the water, making roads near to impassable.

middle 16.5 feet cut smooth and even with the ground. Mr. Danforth's road inspector, senior surveyor W. Chewitt, made reports that could have been written by a township road superintendent today. He found that some hollows needed filling, that some "knowles" and hillocks needed levelling and that there were rotten logs, stumps, and underbrush to be removed. Bridges and causeways were generally good "although a few could be improved."

While the road was a good one for winter travel, Chewitt reported that the four settlers along the route would not be able to keep the road in good repair for the summer months. In the four months since the work party had gone through, he noted 30 trees had fallen and needed to be cleared off the road. Chewett went on

The abundance of trees in the new country made it quite easy to build corduroy roads

to recommend that government lands be divided into 200-acre parcels for settlers and that none of the land be set aside for clergy or the Crown, since this made gaps in road maintenance.

The government implemented a variety of measures to speed up the opening of the new lands. It introduced the Statute of Labour law in 1793, which required inhabitants to contribute up to 12 days of labour per year for road and bridge construction. This proved to be a problem since landowners were not required to do labour proportional to the assessed value of their property. For the next 120 years, the need for better and improved roads would become far greater than the expertise offered through this conscripted labour.

Another law that reflected the dire need for improved roads was the Stump Act of 1800, which set convicted drunks to work with axe and logging chains removing stumps. Yonge Street, which runs north out of Toronto, showed a visible improvement.

Initially, settlers cut down the great trees to allow pedestrian traffic through, and went back later to pull out or burn away stumps, trim back the quick-growing undergrowth, and bridge the streams with the cut logs. The system was set up for the pioneer spirit: those who would pull together to get the job done. From this group came the pathmaster, one chosen from among the settlers to organize and guide the rest of the settlers in their common task of road building.

The idea of a pathmaster was a good one but had its drawbacks. There were as many different opinions about what constituted a good road and how to achieve it as there were pathmasters. But they all faced the same problems of rough terrain, swamps, muskeg, rocks and hills, and heavy forest cover.

Road makers used a variety of solutions to master the terrain and make it passable. The abundance of trees made it easy to develop the corduroy principle. Trees felled along the newly opened road were laid parallel and at right angles to the direction of travel to form a firm surface over muddy depressions or streams. This road was very uncomfortable to ride on and extremely hard on the wagon. Winter proved to be an easier season in which to keep the roads clear. With no vegetative growth and lots of snow to pack down over the rough spots, the transporting of goods was considerably easier than in the summer months when the roads became soggy and rotted.

Wherever the snow would drift too high for easy passage, some travellers would take down the rail fencing and detour through the fields, around the drifts. For some time thereafter the priority on roads slackened. Farmers used the summer months to clear and work their land and moved their products, primarily grain crops, by sleigh over the more passable winter trails.

By the mid-1800s, the demand was back ever stronger for more improved roads. The government had allocated massive funding to improve both waterways/canals and railway systems, thereby allowing settlers to get their products to the larger settlements. But it had neglected to show the same concern and financial support for the road systems that would allow those same settlers to get to the newly refurbished canals and newly built railways.

Two solutions to the massive job of road construction became popular. Thomas Telford developed the concept of a heavy stone foundation with two or three layers of tightly packed smaller stones. John McAdam of Great Britain took the concept one step further. He recognized the load-bearing capacity of soil when kept dry and compact and capitalized that with the crowning of the road for drainage. But the real plus was the development of an impervious surface, which McAdam produced with a clean layer of broken stone of a fairly small, uniform size. Traffic would not only pack the stones tighter together but also create a binding dust which would further decrease water's attempt to penetrate this

surface. Though this created a strong and durable road surface it was extremely expensive since gravel was made by breaking rocks by hand. Some townships in Ontario were fortunate to have gravel deposits to help offset the costs.

The second alternative was plank roads, which were a modified version of the primitive corduroy roads. Long parallel wooden stringers or beams, with thick wooden planks nailed at right angles to the stringers, were covered with a thin layer of sand. This provided a smooth, fairly durable surface, easily and cheaply built. The first plank road was built in 1835 on a stretch of highway leading east from Toronto. This method was more practical from both a resources and pocket-book point of view.

Plank roads were popular for only 20 years. Their big advantages were not limited to their inexpensive construction or comfortable ride. Travellers could also attain a speed of 8 miles per hour as compared to 2 miles per hour on other existing roads.

Plank roads flexed with the weight of heavily loaded wagons, loosening the nails holding the planks to the stringers. Horse hooves and wagon wheels worked the planks down a half inch each year. Plank roads were abandoned after the mid-19th century.

Local papers were full of ideas and suggestions about how to build a good road. An excerpt from the *Huron Signal*, Goderich, written in 1848 by a 'Huron Settler' outlines a foolproof way of building a road which would open up the Huron district to make it the garden of Upper Canada. "The road should be dug in the centre where practicable, to the depth of one foot, for, say one rod or 16 1/2 feet, or if you will 25 feet in width, my estimate supposes the lattter. The surface levelled where dug, then have ready prepared bundles of brushwood, put up in bunches 8 feet long, and 1 foot in diameter, these bundles are to be firmly held together and laid end to end across the road laying solid on the ground and as close to each other as possible; they are to be made of fresh twigs cut in a green of growing state and may be in size from one half inch to three or four inches in circumference. When laid they will have the appearance of brushwood logs all the same size, which two men can handle with ease either in loading them on sleighs or wagons to take them to the road and lay them in it; they should be laid with a little loose brush and then the stuff that was dug out should be laid upon them a little more from the sides, till there is at least 18 inches of the clay or mud covering the brush logs, and so excluding them from the action of the air which if properly managed, would ensure their lasting. I think for the time I stated, 50 years."

In response to the Huron Settler's road design a Fullarton correspondent had a different idea. He had studied the reconstruction of the Huron road between the Wilmont Line and Goderich (1835-1836).

In 1835 the Canada Company removed the continuous log-

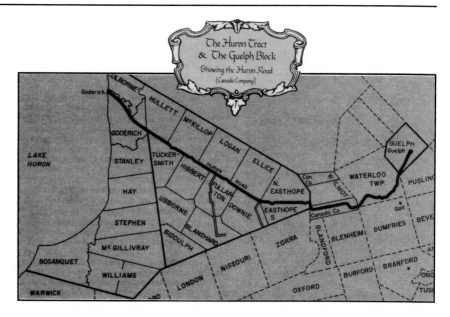

way from the Wilmont Line to Goderich, and during that year and in 1836, laid the foundation of the new road. A 20 foot strip in the centre of the allowance of road was cleared of stumps, and the earth thrown up made the road 18 inches higher in the centre than at the sides – thus our term highways. Water tables were formed six inches to one foot deep. Outlets had to be seen to, although many complaints revolved around the culverts not being deep enough to take the water away and far too narrow for the volume. The unnamed Fullarton correspondent to the *Huron Signal*, on January 5, 1849, recommended draining the low side of numerous long stretches betweenWilmot and Goderich with outlets (deeper than the drains and culverts) built with framed timber and covered with hewn timber and at least 4 feet wide so that the water tables on the high side could empty themselves. The writer developed his road-building theory by explaining that "the road bed must be dug out with the earth thrown on to the sides and on the level bed 6 inches of gravel are to be laid With two yoke of oxen and a heavy elm roller 13 feet long, go twice over the gravel, then of the earth from the sides I would scatter 6 inches on the gravel, and roll it twice, put on 6 inches more of gravel and roll twice, over which I would throw the cleaning of the water tables and give it a finish with the roller".

As the railroad completed links between the cities and into the hinterland the low status of roads was further eroded. The steel road was passable all year round monopolizing passenger services as well as the more profitable freight trade and mail. Individuals and all levels of government invested in railways rather than in creating better roads. Local governments had the road network dumped back into their laps.

Artist's rendition of an elm log

Cities were not without their road problems too. Both commercial and industrial centres demanded more street transport. In Toronto and Montreal innovative minds combined horsepower with rail ingenuity and introduced horse-drawn streetcars. But it was a short-lived venture. The horses' hooves chewed up the road surface between the rails. Horse cars wore down the macadam, while cedar blocks, bricks and cobblestone were too slippery when wet. It was at this time too, that the connection between cholera and sewage forced urban areas to clean up; the increasing amount of horse debris was part of the problem. City health officials and engineers tried a variety of pavement surfaces with the emphasis on a smooth surface that could be easier to keep clean.

With the growth of the urban areas, the demand for fresh vegetables and dairy produce encouraged the development of market farms. These producers required year-round, quick access to the cities. Since railways were expensive and not always running between the smaller communities and the larger urban areas, the push was on again for an improved network of quality roads.

A Good Thing

Good Roads Association

It was during the late 1800s that a handful of agitators began petitioning both residents and all levels of government about the virtues of a well-built road network.

There were examples of ingenuity and foresight. In an experimental move the New Jersey legislature enacted a law in 1892 to set apart certain roads to be kept at the expense of the county. Union County set aside 35 miles of roads and issued $35,000 in bonds to pay for macadamizing. Real estate doubled in price along these routes and towns got busy raising funds to build branch lines to the county roads.

Andrew Pattullo, editor of the *Woodstock Sentinel Review* and a member of the Ontario provincial legislature, was a man of vision. He realized that the development of the country would depend on the people and the means at their disposal to create a great country. To improve the lot of the people, better roads must be built and public resistance to the initial cost burden could be overcome with education.

Pattullo, along with Dr. P. E. Doolittle, president of the Canadian Automobile Association, formed the Good Roads Association in 1893 as a temporary framework through which agitators could organize and become more effective in their lobbying of government and the public. In 1899 the association was transferred from being a voluntary association to being a county government organization. This was a crucial step that lent more power to the issue of better roads. The organization was now more than a handful of men agitating for good roads. It now had affiliation with 11 counties in the province and made the question of acquiring good roads an issue for everyone.

At the annual meeting in 1899 Pattullo addressed a group of 50 delegates from across Ontario with these words: "We have spent hundreds of millions of dollars in this country on the transportation question. Building railways, deepening our canals, providing better facilities for cold storage on steamboats. On both sides of transportation we have been spending enormous sums of money. We should go further. We should go beyond the main arteries of trade and get to the little arteries which are the rural highways of the country and until we do that we have not solved the transportation problems."

Another figure that stands ahead of all others is A.W. Campbell. Fondly dubbed 'Good Roads Campbell', the former city engineer of St. Thomas was appointed Provincial Inspector of roads in 1896 as a direct result of pressure from the Good Roads Association to create the position. He had the dubious honour of travelling around the province lecturing on the economic and social benefits of good roads and demonstrating proper road-building techniques on short spans of road. He minced no words and was often quoted in the press as having condemned local roads and offered sound advice on how to rectify the situation.

Campbell voiced strong support for municipalities organizing the layout of their counties, taking advantage of heavily travelled areas and building up where the need warranted it most.

Well into the twentieth century, roads were built without benefit of the new mechanization. Animal power broke the sod. This method was used as late as the 1930s in Saskatchewan. Photo Courtesy of the Saskatchewan Archives Board No. R-A 4049(1)

Once the sod is broken, two-wheeled scrapers remove the dirt to the side leaving a deep depression to be filled with stone and creating a solid foundation for the road. Photo courtesy of the Saskatchewan Archives Board R-B3720(1)

Addressing members at the annual meeting in 1899, Campbell said: "I think municipal councils should lay down a plan. It is an easy matter to prepare a diagram of the township; sketch the roads out and classify them. About one third of the roads are main roads subject to the traffic of the township largely. These roads must be built in a more expensive manner, greater width and depth than the others. There is another class used by only the neighbourhood and leading to those main roads. The third class are back concessions which don't require, by any means, the same treatment as the other roads."

Campbell went on to outline further ideas for municipal councils to consider: "Specify the width; that the main roads be 24 feet in width, the next roads 20 feet and concessions 18 feet; and let us specify that the roads be graded uniformly and stripped for

a rise of one inch to a foot from the edge to the centre of the road. Let us have them graded so that they will be uniform and specify how the grading and levelling shall be done, how the stones and the gravel shall be prepared. Specify what shall be a load of gravel, a cubic yard or a yard and a half. Specify the number of loads that would constitute a day's work then issue the orders to the foremen and see that they are carried out accordingly. Increase the size of the beats to sections as it is done in some townships, placing one pathmaster or commissioner in charge of each. Appoint this man by bylaw and keep him in office and make him as concientious an officer as the clerk or treasurer. Men can be found with sufficient

knowledge or ability to do the work if you secure them with the position permanently. You will have a plan and they will be going on your authority as officers to carry it out. And you will find there is very little trouble in organizing the spaces. If this could be done what a help it would be to the roads and to the people in the township."

From the 1899 convention came a list of recommendations that reflected the beginning of a formal commitment to a policy that would aim to provide "Good Roads" for the province.

The recommendations were as follows: there is a necessity for provincial aid to continue the Good Roads movement; aid should be given to municipalities to build gravel, macadam, or other permament roads; such roads should be constructed to a standard approved by government and subject to the approval of competent commissioners; the importance of good roads as a system of transportation should be recognized and; there should be a state policy to assist in the improvement of roads.

The group also demanded that members return to their municipalities and work to have a bylaw promoting four-inch rims on wagon wheels. The condemnation of the narrow rims was for good reason. They cut into the roads and left ruts which filled with water.

During his tenure as Provincial Inspector of Roads, Campbell addressed over 500 public meetings which included different farm groups as well as municipal councils. He condemned the use of

The Fathers of Canadian Good Roads

A. W. CAMPBELL
closed a lifetime achievements in highway improvement as Federal Commissioner of Highways.

DR. DOOLITTLE
president of the Canadian Automobile Association, raised the first Canadian Good Roads Fund back in the days of the high-wheeler bicycle and was the chief advocate of the Trans-Canada Highway.

ANDREW PATTULLO
Who along with Dr. Doolittle started the first Canadian Good Roads Association activities.

HON. G. S. HENRY
in the 'early' days of the Good Roads movement, took his political life in his hands by open advocacy, in season and out, of Good Roads. 'Honest George' went on to be premier of Ontario from 1930 to 1934.
Ministry of Transportation 18295

appointed pathmasters and said that their work as a whole was very unsatisfactory. The *Huron News Record's* account of his April meeting with the Clinton council in 1896 reads as follows: "While a dozen different pathmasters will give a dozen different opinions as to gravel and good road making, he wanted to say most emphatically that sand or earth would never make good roads; sand simply holds the rain; earth makes mud – with traffic then the roads are destroyed. First-class gravel should be used and that of a uniform size. Pathmasters and the duties of street inspectors should be boiled down. Under present conditions it is as useless to think of building good roads as it would be to expect the progressive farmer to return to the ancient sickle for harvesting and the ancient flail for threshing." The Statute of Labour also came under fire when Campbell related that the quality of the

work was very poor compared to the results when the law was first initiated.

Campbell firmly believed, along with Pattullo, that road building should be left in the hands of a trained road superintendent and that consistent road-building techniques be used.

Campbell continued to support the cause for better roads after he was appointed Federal Deputy Minister of Railways and Canals and chairman of the Intercolonial Railway Commission in 1910. His comment in the *Toronto Globe* after his appointment reflected his enthusiasm for the topic of transportation: "I look forward to a more intimate and practical knowledge of the entire field of transportation . . . my energies and sympathies will always be retained by the Good Roads Movement."

Everyone had a stake in the concept of better roads. Even

Good Roads – 1920 and 1921 photographs illustrate the before and after development of a Colborne Township road (Huron County).

the horses were given a voice, albeit one with a human lilt: "If the horses and other livestock were able to talk, what a tale of suffering they would tell! Wading knee deep in mud, climbing steep hills and jumping bridges nearly ready to collapse have been the necessities of going to town for every farm horse once upon a time during his life. For every road has experienced its evil days no matter how well it may now be improved. Who suffers? The horse suffers personal injury; the farmer and other industries only suffer financially" (printed in the *Huron Signal*, Goderich, February 18, 1904).

Improved roads were the way to prosperity for both industry and individuals. Farmers driving fattened stock to market had to calculate the weight lost on the trail and the drop in profits averaged $100 per capita per annum. Farmers in 1904 were paying an average of 25 cents, per ton, per mile to get their products/crops to town while the rate by rail was 7 cents. Agitators were quick to point out that if the money lost due to poor roads was directed towards expert road building, within ten years the roads would be in such a state as to prevent the loss of every cent.

Education was one of the keys to better roads. At the first International Good Roads Congress held in Port Huron, Michigan on July 2 and 3, 1900, 80 delegates from across the United States as well as A. W. Campbell of the Provincial Road Commission, Toronto and Andrew A. Pattullo, MPP, Woodstock visited the day long, on-site road construction demonstration. The *Farmers Advocate* of July 16, 1900 gave a detailed account of the methods promoted in road construction. Speakers included farmers, who when faced with increased taxation for better roads, were more

This muddy road of 1904 illustrates the need for better roads.

concerned that the move for better roads be stepped up, because better roads meant more profits and, in the end, lower taxes for maintenance.

A sample of road was under construction under the direction of E. G. Harrison, an American road expert from Washington, D. C. "The road consisted of a half mile of macadam put down on loose sandy soil. That is never good except after a rain and then only for light vehicles. A line of street railway occupied the centre of the street, and the macadam road was put down only on one side of the track."

Among the pictures included with the article in the *Farmers Advocate* was one showing the condition of the street on the side not treated. The notched markings were made by the wheels of the traction engine that was used to haul the metal (broken stone) from the crusher to the road bed. Equipment was now an integral part of making good roads and nothing was lost in describing the equipment as well as the methods employed. The stone crusher was at work at the end of the road and beside the railroad – where the stone had been brought by rail from farming lands some distance out. The crusher used was a modern pattern fitted with a convex jaw to prevent the possibility of flat stones going through without being broken into the desirable size.

Parade float theme (1915) – The banner on this July 1st parade float reads
"WE ARE THE PEOPLE – GIVE US GOOD ROADS"

"The stone is crushed to a size that will pass through a two-and-a-half inch ring, and screened into three grades; coarse, one and a half inch, and fine screenings and dust."

"In preparing the sandy road bed for the material, it is moistened and rolled with a ten-ton traction roller until it is firm and uniform. There is next put down a ridge of moist adhesive clay along the outside edge of where the macadam road is to be built. The next operation is to put down four inches of the two-and-half-inch stone. On this a light dressing of screenings or sand is spread and moistened and the rolling commenced."

"As the rolling is continued more screenings are applied until three inches have been put on. This is moistened and rolled until the spaces between the particles are filled so thoroughly that the pieces cease to creep, move, or give way before the roller as it passes over."

"When finished the road will slant a half-inch to the foot towards the ditch, and the clay ridge will be removed so that the water will readily shed itself from the surface."

Drainage was not ignored during this exercise. It was emphasized from the outset that drainage either by a well-kept open ditch or tile drain was the first priority. The next move of importance was to prepare a firm foundation. The article printed in the *Farm-*

ers Advocate went on with more specific points: "Sand or clay is suitable if firmly compacted. Broken stone is put on top and rolled extensively to bind the mass together. It was explained that the top layer of chips and dust, when rolled in a moist condition, forms a waterproof roof and, after a few months, becomes set similiar to cement. It requires judgement to decide when sufficient rolling has been given, as where the water line is only a short distance from the surface excessive rolling causes it to rise to the road-bed in sufficient quantity to cause a weakening of the foundation."

The estimated cost of $2,500 per mile would be affected by the availability of material and labour costs.

A variety of speakers at the congress emphasized the benefits of good roads. A medical doctor claimed that good roads shortened the time it takes to reach rural clients, not to mention making the trip less wearing for both physician and patient. It was also pointed out that some medical men were coming to the conclusion that many cases of nervous diseases and premature aging in women were due to riding over rough country roads.

Passable country roads in all seasons would also enable more young people to travel to and from school, reducing the need to board in towns when completing their education. Good roads would also inspire farmers to improve lawns and paint their houses and barns. The comfort of the city would come to the country.

All these demands for better roads were not lost on the manufacturing sector. Men with an eye to the future and a clever hand could foresee an increased demand for more bicycles, automobiles, buggies, road-making machinery, and many other classes of goods. Some converted part of their agricultural implement plants to manufacture road-building equipment.

Lover's Lane, Saskatoon.

The Companies

Among road makers the name Champion conjures up an image of powerful road-building equipment with a history tied closely to the 'good roads' movement.

The Pennock family firm manufactured agricultural equipment and railway cars. In 1875 the firm began to get involved with road- building equipment with the invention and patenting of the two-wheeled road scraper. Samuel Pennock went on to streamline the scraper idea and invented and patented the first four-wheeled road scraper which was dubbed 'The American Champion' in June of 1877. The following year the family firm, S. Pennock and Sons Company, enlarged their plant at Kennett Square, Pennsylvania to manufacture scrapers and other new road-building equipment.

By 1883, the impact of the demand for better roads was evident in the sharp increase in sales of the American Champion road scraper. Sales leaped from 500 one year to 800 the next.

Samuel Pennock retired in 1886 during an exciting time in the company's history. G. Taft, who was the inventor of a rock-crushing machine and holder of some 400 patents, joined the

Samuel Pennock
Inventor of the first four-wheel grader
in North America

firm as president. The company expanded and bought machinery firms in Ohio, Indiana, and New York. In 1889 a group of buyers reorganized the company under a new name, The American Road Machine Company. Years later, after the introduction of snow plows, the company changed its manufacturing name to American Road Machinery Company, Incorporated. To sell the products, the The Good Roads Machinery Company was created with branch offices across the states from New York and Boston to San Francisco.

Views of the four factories
where 'Good Roads' equipment
was made in 1889.

KENNETT SQUARE

MARATHON N.Y.

DELPHOS OHIO

GROTON N.Y.

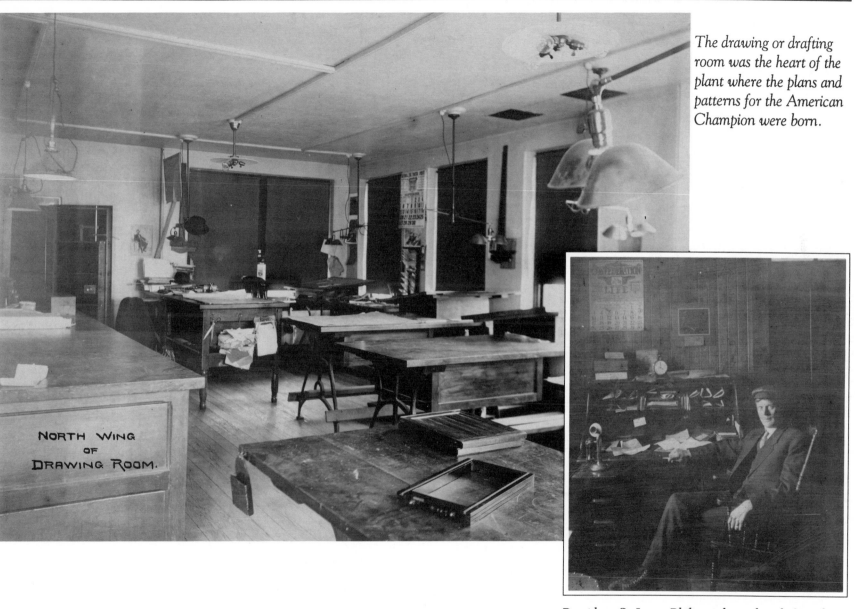

The drawing or drafting room was the heart of the plant where the plans and patterns for the American Champion were born.

NORTH WING OF DRAWING ROOM.

President S. Jones Philips takes a break from his many duties at Kennett Square.

In 1909 managers of the various plants inspect the giant lathes and equipment that machine all the parts for the graders. At the back left corner of the room is the steam engine which powered the machines by means of a line shaft running above the work stations. A lever engaged the belt from the idler to the drive pulley working the machine.

KENNETT SQUARE, PENNSYLVANIA – The American Road Machinery Company, Inc. was an advanced company for its time. It produced equipment for the road maker. The huge plant was located beside the railway yard for easy access to markets around North America. Pictured here, clockwise from upper left, are inside shots of the plant. The power was generated by coal-fired furnaces which created steam to run the turbines in the engine room. In the detail shop you can see how the equipment was pushed along the assembly line, taking advantage of the ten-ton crane with its 39-foot span to lift heavier pieces. Pictured in the erecting shop room are wooden wheels already wrapped with steel rims. The heated steel would expand and be slipped around the wheels. When cooled it would contract, making for a tight fit.

The Good Roads Machinery Co., Inc.

of Kennett Square, Penna.

Extends

A Most Cordial Invitation
to the Trade
to Inspect
Their Factory
Before Purchase of

ROAD DRAGS
GRADERS
MOTOR GRADERS
GASOLINE ROLLERS
PORTABLE ROCK PLANTS
QUARRY EQUIPMENT
PORTABLE GRAVEL PLANTS
ETC.

Manufactured By

The American Road Machinery Co., Inc.

KENNETT SQUARE, PENNA.

An invite – Trade shows were a popular selling tool for companies. They would post the invite in the local paper and welcome anyone and everyone to see the latest in equipment.
The railcars (c. 1880) would leave Kennett Square, Pennsylvania loaded with road- making equipment such as rollers and crushers.

F. L. Wright had the honour of working as the manager of the 'Introduction of Champion Road Machines' in Canada for the American Road Machine Company. He sold the first early graders – 'American Champion' – as early as 1888 in Cobourg, Uxbridge, and Lindsay, and to the Woodbridge Driving Association. Wright never lost sight of the Champion and became a shareholder in the Dominion Road Machinery Company of Canada, Goderich, in 1916.

In 1892, Copp Brothers of Hamilton became the sole owners of the Canadian rights to manufacture and sell Champion road-making machines.

In 1895, Copp Brothers manufactured the 'Steel Champion' Road Grader, of which approximately 30 were sold in the country to Ingersoll, Guelph, and Rainy River. The following year, 1896, Steel Champions were sold as far east as Charlottetown, P.E.I. and Truro, Nova Scotia, as well as to the Hamilton and Goderich municipalities.

Part of the selling of the road scrapers included demonstra-tions. In Goderich the minutes of the council meeting of June 25, 1896 instructed the clerk to write and thank Copp Brothers of Hamilton, manufacturers of the Champion Road Machine, for the fine demonstration. The demonstration included the construction and gravelling of a street 48 rods long and the scraping of the street known as the Square. The public works committee was so impressed that they bought a road scraper for $235 and took pleas-ure in recommending the same machine to any corporation having streets to make or improve.

John Challen, manager of the Copp firm, expressed an inter-est in forming another company called the Champion Road Ma-chinery Company. He petitioned the Ontario Provincial Secre-tary in November of 1896. This idea was abandoned when Challen bought out Copp Brothers and all their rights to the manufactur-ing and selling of Champion road-making machines. He renamed the firm the Good Roads Machinery Company, which was sepa-rate from the selling agents for the American Good Road Com-pany of that same name.

An exhibit by Copp Brothers, Hamilton, showing off the latest in road-making equipment at the Toronto Fair in 1896. Pictured are John and Eliza Challen and their children George and Minnie.

An excellent situation – Goderich offered an excellent location, close to both rail and water. The trend in the early 1900s was for towns to encourage development by offering loans, tax breaks and guarantees for bonds issued by the firms. Goderich has a unique layout. The core area is an octagon in design and is traditionally called 'The Square'.
Photo courtesy of Mac Campbell Photography

The

Columbia Hotel

THOS. ARNOLD, Proprietor

St. Thomas, Ont.

Nov. 24th 1896

Provincial Secty
Toronto

Dear Sir As I am proposing to form a Company Styled the "Champion Road Machinery Co" - will you please forward to me the necessary forms for prospectus applications for charter etc etc to my address as below.

John Challen
259 York St
Hamilton
Ont -

GOOD ROADS' MACHINERY

JOHN CHALLEN, Manager.

SOLE OWNERS OF THE CANADIAN PATENTS, AND RIGHTS TO THE MANUFACTURE AND SALE OF THE

Celebrated "CHAMPION" Road Making Machines

ROAD MACHINES.
ROCK CRUSHERS.

ROAD ROLLERS.
MUD SCRAPERS.

ROAD PLOWS.
WHEEL AND DRAG SCRAPERS.

SCREENS AND ELEVATORS.

EXHIBIT OF "CHAMPION" ROAD MAKING MACHINERY, TORONTO FAIR, 1896.

HAMILTON, CANADA   Feb'y. 20th, 97.

Assistant Secretary,

Department of the Provincial Secretary,

Toronto, Ont.

Dear Sir:-

I reply to yours of the 17th, inst, would say that we do not intend to go on with the formation of the Company proposed.

You will notice from the enclosed card that the writer is now running the business in his own name, under the caption of the Good Roads Machinery Co. You can therefore regard the matter as disposed of in the meantime,

Very truly yours,

Good Roads Machinery Co.

John Challen
Manager.

In November of 1896, John Challen requested forms from the Ontario government to create a company that would manufacture road-building equipment using the name Champion. Later he reconsidered his plans and bowed to the popular usage of the name 'Champion' by the American Road Machine Company.

Competitors – In 1887 Sawyer & Massey Company was busy making machinery for the road makers of the day.
Below is a steam engine furnished by the short-lived Canadian Road Machine Company of Hamilton.

Sawyer & Massey Co., Limited

HAMILTON, CANADA

For Strictly High-Grade

Engines, Threshers and Road-Making Machinery

1907

A celebration logo – The American Road Machinery Company had this logo developed to show clients its expanding role in the road-building equipment business. The medallions at the top corners were awarded at the New York World's Exposition for excellence in exporting. The dates at the bottom indicate the manufacturing of the first four-wheeled grader named the American Champion and the second date signifies the purchase of the new subsidiary plant in Goderich, with head office in Kennett Square, Pennsylvania.

To increase his edge over a competitor also manufacturing in Hamilton, Sawyer & Massey Company Ltd., Challen requested testimonials from satisfied buyers. There was no doubt that the time of road-building machinery had come. Some municipalities shared ownership of equipment with local Driving Park Associations (race tracks) and sold shares to help finance machinery expenses.

The Good Roads Machinery Company manufactured dump wagons, scrapers, road plows, stone crushers, elevators, bins, road rollers, and galvanized culvert pipes.

John Challen didn't survive the great rush to produce road-building equipment. To appease creditors and the Bank of Hamilton, he dissolved his assets in November, 1907. He didn't leave the business altogether, and later became a sales representative for The American Road Machine Company, Goderich.

In 1908, a group of investors headed by Robert Mancill, Chester Walters, and William Bell of Hamilton, and Samuel Jones Philips and William Voorhees of Kennett Square, Pennsylvania petitioned the Ontario Lieutenant Governor to create a new company: the Canadian Road Machine Company Limited. This new firm bought land, buildings, and machinery left by Challen and, under the guidance of the main investor and president Robert Mancill, started to manufacture Champion Road Machinery.

This company was shortlived and almost two years later, in 1909, surrendered its newly awarded charter to the American Road

Stuck! Because of a swale in the road, left to form a deep mud hole.

Machinery Company Incorporated of Kennett Square, Pennsylvania, which was headed by S. Jones Philips.

Part of the purchase price was used to reimburse the shareholders, who were then offered an opportunity to purchase shares in the American Road Machine Company of Canada Ltd., a subsidiary of the American firm.

The American Road Machine Company of Canada purchased a vacant factory, formerly the Goderich Engine Works and Henderson Bicycle Company (manufacturers of the 'Common-Sense' bicycle in Goderich at the corner of Cambria Road and East Street). They bought in January of 1910, and installed their equipment in February.

One of the major reasons for the move from the Hamilton location was to reduce labour problems. In all the major plants in Hamilton, from steel manufacturers to equipment manufacturers, the unions were demanding, and getting, higher wages. In 1910 workers in Hamilton were paid 25 cents per hour while in Goderich the wage was 15 cents.

Goderich also offered an excellent situation close to both rail and water. It was a trend then for towns to encourage development by offering loans, tax breaks and guarantees for bonds issued by the firms. Goderich had in the past sponsored business ventures yet when the town was approached by the American Road Machine Company to guarantee company bonds, ratepayers were concerned. At a public meeting criticism was aimed at the

Goderich town council for over-extending the resources of the town. Some loans like the one of $5,000 to the Goderich Organ Company had been repaid but a loan of $10,000 to the summer hotel in 1902 was yet unpaid. In guaranteeing the bonds for the American Road Machine Company, the town would not be out of pocket for funds unless the firm ran into difficulties and had to close. In that case the town would be left with the buildings and equipment as well as the repayment of the bonds sold.

A committee of the mayor, Mr. Macklin, and the president of the Board of Trade, Mr. Rumball, visited Kennett Square, to look into the financial affairs of the American firm and ensure that the proposal presented to Goderich was fair. The committee studied the books and visited the banks and the factory itself. They were impressed that the American firm hired only men earning fair wages and no 'boy' was seen at the factory.

C. L. Moore
Vice President & Treasurer

Before the town could establish an agreement with the American Road Machine Company it had to pass a bylaw subject to the vote of ratepayers. It was a complicated affair requiring public meetings and two votes before the bylaw became a reality. The company would be, in a sense, a branch of the American Road Machine Company of Kennett Square, Pennsylvania. While it would be a distinct corporation, it would have in back of it the brains and business experience of the American company.

The Goderich firm would have rights to all the patents controlled by the American Road Machine Company and would make repairs on all the models sold in Canada by both the American and Canadian factories.

Mr. Woods, a representative of the American Road Machine Company, said the company would build everything for the road makers, and in addition would make portable sawmills of a special kind not made elsewhere in Canada. Goderich ratepayers supported the bylaw and a deal was made to support the company.

Robert Mancill moved to Goderich as vice-president of the firm. S. Jones Philips became president of both the Goderich plant and Kennett Square. The board of directors for the American Road Machine Company of Canada Limited included members from large firms located in the United States. Among stockholders associated with the board were J. M. Landenberger, general manager of the Fort Wayne and Delphos, Ohio factories of the American Road Machinery Company; J. R. Manning, manager of the Marathon, New York office and also a member of the export firm of Messrs. Carr & Tyler , which did an extensive export business with foreign countries; and the A. B. Farquhar Company of York, Pennsylvania. They met regularly and drew upon their varied expertise to help solve problems in the company.

Mr. Mancill was replaced as manager by C. L. Moore of Butler, Pennsylvania in 1912. Mr. Moore took an active interest in the community until his retirement in 1922. He was president of the Board of Trade and was involved in the local baseball league.

Mr. Moore was a shrewd businessman and was instrumental in securing several very large contracts. Machinery orders that were too large for the smaller Goderich firm to fill on time were partially filled by the American firm. With the increased demand for road-making equipment the managers decided to look at building a bigger plant or at expansion of some of their departments into other locations. In 1913, the ratepayers of Goderich were asked to vote in favour of another bond issue.

During the successful campaign the *Huron Signal* encouraged readers to vote with these words "Every resident should remember that he lives in this town, not for what he can get out of it, but for what good he can do it and himself at the same time. Remember that each and everyone owes, as a religious duty, to the town in which he or she resides that they do all in their power to make it a bigger, brighter and more successful city or town."

The Canadian factory was a success. In a letter to the *Goderich Signal*, C. L. Moore reported on a visit by the American shareholders in 1914. "For the benefit of all who are interested, and you all are interested in the welfare of this, as well as other industries of our town, the gentlemen who visited us have all taken additional stock, and the financial prospects are brighter and better than they have ever been for the American Road Machine Company of Canada Limited.

The factory became a major employer and in 1915 under a restructuring the firm again changed its name to reflect its change in charter. Now, instead of holding a provincial company charter, it would be called Dominion Road Machinery Company and hold a dominion or federal charter. The firm would prosper with increased access to the new markets across the Dominion of Canada and would not look back as it built better equipment for the better roads of the future.

In 1922 Mr. Keith Hubbard of Catskill, New York replaced C. L. Moore.

Throughout all this management and business reorganization the name Champion was not lost. American Champion equipment, first named in 1878 was still being produced.

Improvements were constantly being made to the horse-drawn graders, but a major breakthrough happened in 1920-1921 when the American Good Road Machinery Company of Kennett Square issued the first motorized road grader. It used a Yuba Ball Tread Tractor with 15 to 25 horsepower, but the price proved too costly and the line was discontinued two years later.

Recognizing a good idea, however, the company redesigned the road grader and road rollers using the cheaper and more available Fordson tractor. The model issued in 1924 was geared to give four times the usual power needed in grading and road rolling.

From 1909 to 1929, most designs and changes originated in head office at Kennett Square, but innovative designs such as the Baby Winner #1 and #2 were also put together at the Goderich plant in 1920.

In 1929 The American Road Machinery Company was facing financial trouble and S. Jones Philips, president of both the American Road Machinery Company and the Dominion Roads Machinery Company, handed in his resignation as president of the Canadian firm. The American firm was bought out in 1932 by a Detroit company and renamed The Good Roads Machinery Company. The company kept busy making rock crushers and gun parts during World War II, but because of a strike and unresolved labour problems the plant closed in 1945, leaving 200 men out of work.

Meanwhile, up in Canada the Dominion Road Machinery Company was doing rather nicely under the direction of shareholders. With its separate charter, it was immune to the problems facing its original parent company back in Pennsylvania. As early as 1924 some of the American directors were beginning to be replaced by Canadian names. In 1929 the controlling interest in the company was bought by T. H. Mitchell, a resident of Goderich. All the American shareholders resigned. Under the direction of T. H. Mitchell, the company continued to manufacture and act as agents for all the equipment any builder of a good

Goderich plant – Both plants shown here are at the south west corner of East Street and Cambria Road in Goderich. The American Road Machinery Company was located here in 1910 and later named the Dominion Road Machinery Company.

The 'brag' sketch for their 1921 catalogue indicated an elaborate and well laid out factory.

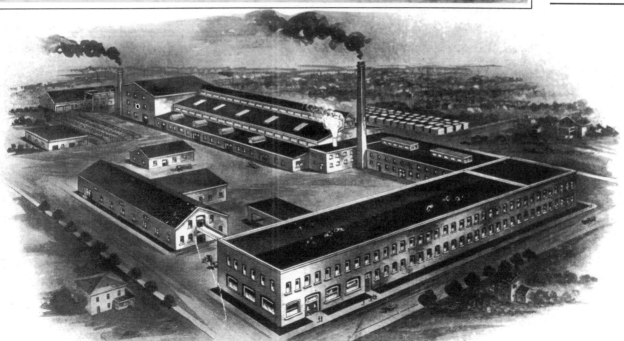

road would need. Despite a short period of rearmament manufacturing during World War II, road-making equipment was always
the priority.

T. H. Mitchell suffered from poor health and one month after
he submitted his resignation to the board, in July of 1937, he died
of a heart attack. Mary Hussey, treasurer, and Rod Johnson, vice-
president, managed the company until W. C. Attridge took over as
president and general manager in 1939.

The plant moved in June, 1943 from East Street to its present
location in the Artcraft Building on Maitland Road in Goderich.

Controlling interest of Dominion Road Machinery Company
was sold on May 7, 1945 to Air Vice-Marshall John A. Sully, C.B.,
A.F.C., recently retired from the Royal Canadian Air Force. Mr.
Sully became president and managing director.

In the early 1950's the company was faced with the decision
of whether or not to tailor the plant to build just road graders and
their attachments. The change was made, and was a major turn in
the history of the plant. In 1977, the name Champion became
more than a trademark and marketing tool when the firm changed
its name from Dominion Road Machinery Company to Champion
Road Machinery Company Limited.

Mr. Sully and later his sons ran the firm until July, 1988. In
August 1988, the company was sold to management and a group of
investors led by Sequoia Associates of Menlo Park, California.

Today Champion Road Machinery Limited still produces the
number-one grader used around the world for road building.

T. H. Mitchell
President and Managing Director
1929 to 1937

Past Presidents and Managing Directors of The Dominion Roads Machinery Company

R. G. Johnston
Vice President & Managing Director
1929 to 1939

W. C. Attridge
President & Managing Director
1939 to 1945

Mary Hussey
Treasurer 1923 - 1945
Managing Director 1937 to 1939

AVM J. A. Sully
President & Managing Director
1945 to 1963

Equipment display of 1911 – The American Road Machine Company of Canada parades out a selection of equipment for prospective buyers. Leading the exhibit is a crusher bin with the screen lowered for transportation, a portable crusher, a Steel Champion grader, and a water sprinkler.

The Carpenter Shop in 1920 — Cores for the sweeper machines were turned on a lathe to cut in a spiral groove. The hickory fibre was wrapped around the roller, then a heavy rope was tightened around to force the fibre into the grooves of the spiral. To the left of the workers is a square timber to be turned and a pile of finshed cores to the right.

60 inch Champion Roller Driven Screen – The idea was simple but the plan for the machine was dependent on strong forged steel. In 1924, blacksmiths were part of the staff needed to forge the steel.

Rock crusher – Graders were not the only road-making equipment produced at Dominion Road Machinery Company in 1924. These rock crushers are destined for Victoria, British Columbia.

Erecting department in 1926 – Improved Steel Champion graders are being crated for export in the Goderich plant. Each grader is packed neatly in two boxes which are bound with iron bands. These are horse-drawn graders destined for Buenos Aires.

Graders

The drag scraper dates back to the 8th century and consisted mainly of a cutting edge to dig into the soil and a pan area to take the load. Power was supplied by draft animals. The cutting edge was forced into the soil by lifting up on the handles. To dump the load the handles were flipped over, turning the pan upside down.

Most designs to improve scrapers so that they would be easier to operate involved the addition of wheels. Another improvement was the addition of a lever to elevate the loader/scraper when filled to reduce friction when being moved to an unloading location.

Road Scraper – To maintain streets and lanes, a small scraper-leveller was used. The inset shows the front blade serrated to chew up bumps in the road and the smaller blade behind would level. There is a platform on the back for the teamster to stand adding weight to the leveller.

Horse drawn scraper blade – The horse pole had holes in the centre and lugs on the side. The mouldboard was attached to the horse pole by means of a pair of rods with hooks on the end. The hooks inserted into the various lugs allowed for adjusting the angle of the board.

The two-wheeled Daisy grader had a wooden frame with a non-reversible blade. The blade could be raised and lowered by means of levers, but the cutting angle was fixed. This model was produced by S. Pennock and Sons of Kennett Square in 1875.

American Road Machine Company was the successor to the S. & M. Pennock & Sons. From the collection of Henry Ford Museum and Greenfield Village Neg. No 2915.

The American Champion

The American Champion made by the Pennock firm of Kennett Square, Pennsylvania in 1878.

The American Champion – First patented in 1875 and improved until 1888, the design remained unchanged until 1925. This particular engraving illustrates the wooden frame carefuly braced and the scraper, bar, cutting edge, axles, and wing rods are of steel. This machine could withstand the strain of five good teams, but could be used in ordinary work with three or even with two teams. The operator could simply press his foot against a latch and push against the wing to change the blade to any desired angle. The position of the blade or pitch adjustment could be adjusted either forward or backward simply by turning the hand-wheel which connects with a screw mechanism. Unlike other types, the cutting blade received its thrust from the rear axle, through a "push frame", instead of being pulled by means of a draw bar as in existing models of that time and future types of road graders.

Another feature on the American Champion was the extension of the rear axle into the ditch side of the road This allowed the horses to stay more on the road and the mould board extended for ditching. By means of a long axle the frame of the machine could be shifted laterally from side to side, which enables cutting down banks and moving a heavy furrow of earth from the side to the middle of the road without the side slipping. It became so popular that soon all horse drawn graders had this feature. The talegate shown here features the patent dates starting in March 9, 1875, 1883,1885, 1886, 1887, and 1888.

The Steel Champion

The Steel Champion was built almost entirely of steel and malleable iron. The American Road Company, successor to the Pennock firm, offered wooden or steel wheels on its graders. By means of a double side adjustment the blade could be shifted laterally from 18 to 24 inches outside of the wheels. This made it the most capable model on the market for cutting down banks, filling ditches, or widening narrow roads. The scraper bar was available in one length or in three sections and had a replaceable edge. From the collection of Henry Ford Museum and Greenfield Village, Neg. No. 2924.

Improved Steel Champion – 1913
Although hard to distinguish on
this photo, the modification
included gears for easier
movement of the blade. It's
weight was only 2,500 pounds
and was powered by 2, 4, or 6
horses.

Improved with off-set tongue on horse pole.

Mr. C.E. Hoag demonstrating the durability,
and road making qualities of the Improved
Steel Champion on Cockburn Island, 1914

Once streets or roads were built, road-makers looked toward the lighter, smaller graders for the upkeep of the streets. Here is a Baby Winner #2 illustrating that point on a street in Goderich, Ontario. In 1920 it's economical features included its lightweight build, 850 pounds, and that it could be drawn by two horses and handled by one man.

The Winner family of small maintenance graders started with lever handles as shown on the right.

The first sale of a Little Winner in Canada was to Charlottetown, Prince Edward Island, in 1911.

The Little Winner was not intended to replace the Standard Reversible machine but rather to work in conjunction with it. It was the business of the Standard machine to dig ditches, build and form roads, while the Little Winners maintained them as smooth, level and well graded. The larger grader required a team of 6 to 8 horses to operate but only two horses were required to operate the Little Winner.

The Big Winner, shown below, is from the next heavier category which features the offset tongue. This larger grader was 3,440 pounds.

C. L. Moore demonstrating his firm's Standard Grader in action on Victoria Street, Goderich in 1922. The scarifier was substituted for the mouldboard in order to do the preliminary ripping up of the old road. Next, 4 inches of gravel was added and rolled, 3 inches of sand material was then applied and rolled, and then the tarvia was applied. Sand over the tarvia was the finishing for what was classed as 'a real road'.

View of Victoria Street, Goderich, looking south from the corner of Nelson Street. You can see the how the scarifier tears up the rough, uneven street, preparing it for 4 inches of gravel and rolling. The scarifier, right, was substituted for the mouldboard and was a simple job to remove, or add on to the grader, for ripping-up jobs.

Graders in Action – It didn't take long before road makers were taking advantage of the power of tractors and using them instead of horses. On the left is a heavier two-man road grader drawn by a Moline oil-pull tractor. Little Winner, below left, is attached to a Fordson tractor. The photograph shows how the operator controlled the tractor from the rear seat of the machine. Next is a Winner Highway Patrol grader attached to the popular Fordson tractor.

Little Winner Grader Attached to a Fordson Tractor
Showing Control of the Tractor by the Operator from the Rear Seat of the Machine

Horses were soon replaced with tractors — Here ditching is being done in 1920 with a Champion Big Winner grader pulled by a Titan Tractor. Notice how high the road is compared to the ditch.

Building Roads – Over the years graders were pulled by any power road makers could get their hands on. In Africa domestic cattle or oxen, pictured left, were harnessed up to a Heavy Duty No. 4 Highway Patrol grader.

The leaning wheels were ideally suited to ditch work, as shown below.

This page from the manufacturer's catalogue says it all. The Champion Highway Patrol Steel Reversible Road Grader was classed as a maintenance grader and was powered by a single team of horses.

Salesmen for the manufacturers were ever introducing new equipment ideas and developments to past purchasers of road-making equipment. John Challen would often write to known buyers for testimonials to promote the qualities of the equipment. Pictured here is a sample of one of the many letters Challen wrote during his years with the American Road Machine Company of Canada Limited, Goderich.

Sales of equipment were not limited to domestic markets but included sales to countries around the world. This line of Highway Patrols is being prepared for shipment to Argentina. Horse-drawn equipment was sold by the hundreds to countries such as New Zealand and Australia well into the 1930s. Parts for those machines were sold as late as the 1950s to such places as Cape Town, South Africa and Northern Ontario.

Champion Multiplane No. 10
Tractor Drawn

A one-man, one-control Maintainer for earth and gravel roads was a practical machine for retread and mulch method surfaces. By the arrangement of the blades, the surface material is forced across the road four times and finally spread in an even layer, thus filling up all depressions and shearing off the bumps and ridges. The original design of the wooden drag was without the back wheels.

Duplex Road Maker and Maintainer

The Duplex Road Maker and Maintainer is a combination of several machines in one and is designed to correct drainage and at the same time form a roadway that is free from ridges, waves, and ruts.
The original design was patented in Omaha but rights were obtained for Dominion Roads Machinery Company Limited in Goderich, Canada, to manufacture and sell.

The Duplex's wide capacity could maintain a roadway up to 26 feet in width. It would clean out the ditch, form the slope, create the shoulder, and maintain the driving surface at a single round.

Powered Graders

By 1915 designers realized that power behind the blade would be an efficient use of power. One of the first pictures showing this concept is from a catalogue produced by Kennett Square, Pennsylvania, dated 1915. With the faster moving truck pushing the blade, repair work was done quicker and more economically.

The Champion plow was fitted for attachment to various trucks and used not only for road work but at landfill sites levelling ashes and other materials. It was successful in reclaiming land from the lake. Attached to the front of the tractor or truck, it would reach out over the water and deposit material farther than it could be placed by any other method.

Monarch Road Maintenance Machine

The Monarch machine was designed to do better maintenance work at a low operating cost. It was recommended for attachment to trucks of two ton capacity or greater. Each unit was self contained so that in event of breakage the part in question could be changed in a few minutes without disturbing the rest of the attachment.

The following facts were used to illustrate the money-saving feature of the Monarch:

A "Monarch" installed on a pneumatic-tired truck:
Labour(driver) per day $6.00
Gasoline, 10 gallons at .23 per gal. $2.30
Oil, 2 quarts at .25 .... .50
Truck and Scraper deterioration $3.00
Tire deterioration...$3.00
Total $14.80
Horse Drawn Scrapers
6 teams and drivers at $6.00 per day $36.00
Deterioration of scrapers at .50 each $3.00
Total $39.00

By comparing these figures the saving of $24.20 per day over a period of a 20 working days a month would amount to more than the cost of a Monarch.

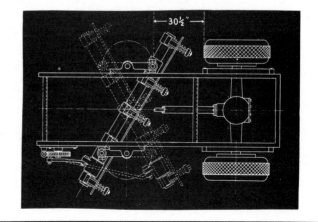

The Yuba Ball Tread Tractor Grader

The first authentic power grader was built in 1920-21 and was powered by a Yuba Ball Tread tractor. This tractor was unique in that it featured tracks that ran on ball-bearing races instead of track rollers. It weighed 6,750 pounds and cost $2,900. This grader line was short lived because of the expense of building it.

Champion 1924 Fordson Power Unit

NEW!

Good Roads Motor Grader

Here, at last, is a motor grader that meets actual working requirements. It is the mature product of years of patient field research — free from the inevitable faults of machines hastily contrived to meet a new market.

Compact in design. Easy to operate. Staunchly contructed to give it the stamina for tough jobs and long service. Side members of frame are heaviest 6-inch ship channel.

Most motor graders are limited to light work, because their Fordson power plants cannot develop the required 'punch'. In the Good Roads Motor Grader the Fordson is geared to give four times usual power in grading work.

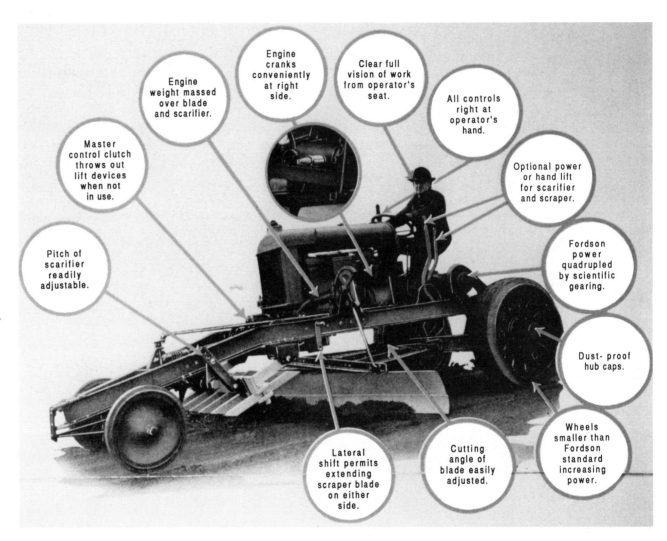

(promotional material from Dominion Road Machine Company Limited, Goderich, Ontario for the Fordson grader designed in Kennett Square, Pennsylvania.)

The latest in road equipment was always a feature at parades. At the Centennial festivities in Goderich in 1927 the newest power grader was dressed in bunting. Since the Dominion Road Machinery Company Limited did not yet make this type of power grader in their plant until 1928, this particular model was shipped in from Kennett Square, Pennsylvania, for the occasion. From 1901 to 1929 all designs and changes originated in the head office of Kennett Square, Pennsylvania and stopped because of financial troubles. The banner reads – The Evolution of Good Roads.

Powered graders were a popular item for progressive councils. In 1928 the City of Peterborough took proud possession of its new E-Z Lift Champion Motor grader powered by a McCormick-Deering Industrial tractor with 10-20 horsepower.

Early pavement was created by laying two ridges of gravel on the road. Passing over this, a truck tanker pours hot asphalt in the space between the ridges. The grader operator drives up behind, turning one furrow of gravel into the asphalt and gently mixing the materials together with each pass of the grader. The sun finishes the job by curing the material.

The crawler models were never really popular because they were expensive as well as difficult to handle when working in snow and ice. Stones were another problem for the track system. This particular model was powered by a McCormick-Deering Model 20 Trackson Crawler Tractor with E-Z Lift Worm and Gear on draw bar and scarifier.

The scarifier was an option on many models and allowed for easy ripping of bumps on the roads. Made of high-grade tool steel, they were easily changed individually with a simple clamp and bolt system. Another feature was the side cranking to start the engine, which avoided danger to the operator. The vibration was reduced by mounting the operating platform on springs.

62 Everything for the RoadMaker

Attachments to the graders allowed road builders of the day to use their equipment for a greater variety of jobs, or for simplifying others. The addition of a power takeoff with clutch lever allowed power belts to be used to drive crushers, as shown above.

The Champion Road Float, left, which attaches to the Power Maintainer in place of the single blade, is actually a machine in itself. The purpose is to bring back to the surface of the road the material displaced by traffic, as well as to float it evenly over the surface. The machine was also used to spread or level new gravel. The rear blade could be placed at a height to allow the gravel to pass under it to the depth desired. It replaces mouldboards with additional adjustable spring attachments. It is operated by the usual blade control.

Champion Hydraulic Maintainer – The township of East Wawanosh purchased one of the newest designs in graders which featured hydraulic lift controls. First introduced in 1936, it was the forerunner of the graders of today. One of the options was a closed-in cab to protect the driver from the weather, and was made on the spot according to the buyer's request.

64 Everything for the RoadMaker

Tandem Drive – The Champion Hydraulic Maintainer underwent more improvements and offered Octopus 8-wheel or dual tandem drive in 1939. The gear case was located between the wheels, resulting in the power being transmitted to each of the wheels in equal proportion and giving more power with less waste. This Huron County grader was purchased in 1939, but the single and dual designs were offered for many years after the tandem was introduced.

'You can't beat a Champion' – The father of the hydraulic grader, Rod G. Johnston, made a major addition to the Champion line of graders. The advent of the hydraulic system allowed more ease of blade movement and more power for the jobs at hand. Pictured here on the corner of St. David Street and Cambria Road in Goderich is a test of the hydraulics. The blade and gear unit are in an almost upright position for cutting back banks.

66 Everything for the RoadMaker

Box frame – Always under scrutiny, designers made further major changes — this time to the frame. Instead of using the two single steel front frame pieces, they moved them closer together and created the box frame. With the extra support there was greater strength. This 'mono-member' box frame was offered to the road builders in 1940 and this design is still used today.

Graders that plow rings around trucks – The promotional brochures were filled with a multitude of features and options for graders. This hydraulically operated diesel-powered Champion grader was purchased by Stanley Township in Huron County in 1940.

Dominion Road Machinery Company Limited offered an extensive number of grader designs with a full complement of options. Gas or diesel – 22 to 66 horse power – 10,000 to 20,500 pounds – leaning front wheels, mono-member box frames, chain driven tandem drive, hydraulic or mechanical operation, fully reversible mouldboard – all the best features of the most modern designs. Among the optional equipment were scarifiers, electric lights, starter and horn, spotlights, oil mix mouldboards, snow plow and wing, hood sides and winter front for engine, muffler, odometer, heater, windshield wiper, electric fan, and tire chains.

Once World War II started, steel was in limited supply and production was temporarily halted in 1941 while the plant went into the production of materials for the war effort.

Crushers

With the increasing demand for sand and gravel there came a corresponding demand for modern machinery to produce these materials. Where there were deposits of sand and gravel it was a simple matter to strip the topsoil away and remove the materials. In other areas, that were not so fortunate, labourers were involved in manually breaking the stone to the desired diameter.

The crushers were manufactured in the late 1800s. The Jaw was the first design for crushing and it was not until the 1930s when the gyratory machine was introduced. The jaw type proved to be the better machine and was more widely produced. The Champion crusher was made entirely of steel. In the crushing of the blue boulders or so-called hard heads found in gravel, the strength of the crusher was the main feature. The jaw crusher was driven by direct drive while the gyratory crusher was driven with a countershaft through bevel gears which wore rapidly, frequently broke and consumed a great deal of power. Another feature of the jaw design was the reduction of friction when the power was applied in such a way by means of a double cam that the moving jaw made two movements while the fly wheel revolved once.

Road engineers were very explicit about the size and cleanliness of the gravel needed to make a proper road. The gravel shaker sifted out the dirt and sand and in some cases was used in the washing of the gravel.

The shaker screen was normally used in the washing process. Water would be applied the entire length and with the scrubbing action of the shaker the material was cleaned.

The rotating or drum screen was used in crushing plants and with a variety of screen sizes could offer many grades of gravel .

Where there were no gravel deposits labourers were hired to break stone for road building. Here Chinese workers are preparing gravel for a road bed at Camp Petawawa, 1917.
National Archives of Canada – neg. no. C-68868

Permanent crusher site – Valleyfield, Quebec had a Champion No. 4 crusher set up on site in 1898. Two-wheeled carts would bring the stone and deposit it into the crusher. An elevator would take the crushed stone up to the rotating screens where it would be graded into the two bins below.

Portable Rock Crusher – This is a side view of a No.15 Mounted Champion rock crusher and elevator. The design for this model was patented in December of 1898.

Quarry work – Champion No 5 Crushing plant erected in Outremont Quarry, Montreal, Quebec, September of 1903.

The Good Roads Machinery Company, Limited

HAMILTON, CANADA

Our No. 4 "Champion" Mounted Rock Crusher with Elevator and Chute Screen

The very latest "Up-To-Date," Portable Mounted outfit manufactured

Patented March 22nd, 1900.   Patented June 7th, 1904

Steel Elevator with new patented arrangement for taking up slack of

"CHAMPION"
Rock
Crushers
Elevators
Revolving
Screens
Street Mud
Cleaners
Road
Graders
Road
Rollers
Macadam
Spreading
Wagons
Road
Plows
Portable or
Stationary
Engines
Wheel and
Drag
Scrapers, etc.

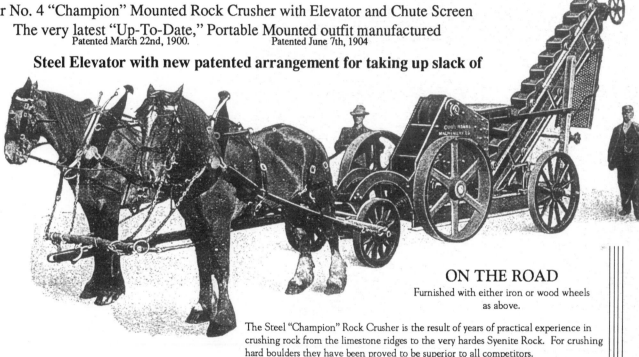

ON THE ROAD

Furnished with either iron or wood wheels
as above.

The Steel "Champion" Rock Crusher is the result of years of practical experience in crushing rock from the limestone ridges to the very hardes Syenite Rock. For crushing hard boulders they have been proved to be superior to all competitors.

Send for the latest printed matter and our 1905 Calendar to

Good Roads Machinery Co., Limited, John Challen, President and General Manager.

Address – Late Killey Beckett Works, 144 York Street, Hamilton, Ont.

Portable Crusher in action – The portable crushers were taken to where the best deposits of stone were. Note the single tray screen to allow for two grades of gravel from the crusher. The workers are loading the hard heads one at a time into the crusher unit. This particular operation is in British Columbia, 1905.

- SIDE VIEW -
Nº 5 MOUNTED CHAMPION ROCK CRUSHER

Rock crushers got bigger and bigger – On the left is a side view of a No. 5 crusher being built at Kennett Square. The larger model, No 55, below, was two No. 5s joined together.

HOPPER ON
Nº 55 A A CHAMPION ROCK CRUSHER

The Champion No. 3 rock crusher could break up to 12 cord of boulders per day. This model was purchased by the town of Huntsville on August 1, 1908 and was built by The Canadian Road Machine Company of Hamilton. This photo shows councillors admiring the equipment. Note the single belt power from the steam engine to the right.

Crusher in the making – Plants were busy making huge steel crushers at the turn of the century. R. G. Johnston, of Dominion Road Machinery Company Limited commented that in the early part of the century manufacturers of road-making equipment had more demand for crushers than for graders. This photo from Kennett Square is of a quarry crusher.

1912 Stationary Gravel Unit – In gravel pits workers shovelled gravel into the elevator and the screened gravel was stored in bins to be loaded onto trucks. This model had a 40-ton capacity.

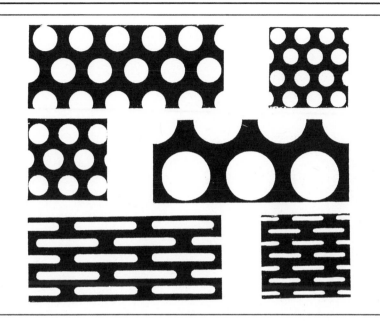

Screens – There were different perforated screens required for different grades of gravel. The plates were usually made with round perforations but under certain conditions, where it was necessary to screen very closely, the oblong holes were preferred.

The crusher screen below was made in Goderich and came complete with a dust jacket (located on the left end of the screen).

More gravel – This large Champion crushing, screening, and washing plant located in Brantford could produce 60 cubic yards of gravel per hour. In Brantford it was essential that the material be clean for concrete work as well as road building. Manufacturers supplied new design ideas for elevators to meet special requirements in the gravel pits and quarries of the purchasers.

Ready for shipment – A complete crushing, screening, and washing unit is loaded for shipment from Dominion Road Machinery Company Limited of Goderich. Purchasers were able to buy the power too, as you can see from the steam engine. Note how the stack has been lowered and the screen unit is lashed below the elevator on the railway car.

Rock crusher – Boss and Brazier contractors operated this crusher, screen, and washing unit outside of Goderich in Colborne Township (1915).

82 Everything for the RoadMaker

Crushing, screening plant – This small plant was set up on the Maitland River flats and was operated by the town of Goderich. Horses were used to pull the drag scrapers around the pit area, drawing the gravel over to the crushing unit.

Installing a Crushing Plant

Installing a crushing plant was no small job. In 1921 the Dufferin Construction Company Ltd. of Toronto set up a crushing plant in Nelson Township for the construction of the provincial highway.

The photos on the preceding page show how the road was built into the area. Then the plant was set up complete with rail line. A closer view of the installation of the crusher unit itself, is shown in the lower left corner. These photos were taken over a short period of time, the first on July 30 and the installation of the crusher on August 19, 1921.

Below is the finished plant in operation.

Sand and gravel machinery – The Markham Ontario Sand and Gravel (Miller Paving) had an outfit like this one utilizing a dredging system to wash the gravel through the crusher and screening machine.

Friction control on side loader – This cut shows the front view of a side loader attached to a crusher. There is a clutch on the side loader for stopping and starting it, without stopping the crusher. The man has his hand on the clutch control. The side loader discharges on a screen and the large stones go into the crusher, the smaller ones into the elevator and up to the revolving screen on top of the bins.

Settling tank rock crusher – This Champion rock crusher and conveyor belt came equipped with a settling tank and was set up for the H. L. Conlin Company in the late 1930s.

A crusher in action – Here is a cut away of a crusher in action with a revolving screen. Th arrows indicate the direction of gravel through the unit.

Road Plows

Road plows were designed to break out hard soil for road construction or for hard-pan plowing. Their operation was similiar to that of a farm plow except these were of heavier construction and ran deeper. They were pulled by 4 to 6 horses and later on a tractor. They nearly always required two men to operate – one on each plow handle.

Above are two examples of road plows. The top one with the spike was used for harder ground.

Snow Plows

A highway, whether it be a city street or country road, is made to be used every day of the year. It cannot be used in winter if it is filled with snow.

Mail, express, fuel, and supplies must be moved in winter the same as in summer. It is just as important, therefore, that city streets and main country roads be kept free of snow so that traffic can pass over them as it is that railroads be kept open.

It costs money to remove snow from a public thoroughfare, but it costs a great deal more not to remove it. This cost strikes in two directions; first, the enormous expense due to the congestion of traffic in cities, as well as in populous country districts, which cost can hardly be estimated. A few hours delay in the opening of a street frequently means losses running into thousands of dollars. Second, experience has shown that large repair bills in the maintenance of highways are directly due to the non-removal of snow. A much larger percentage of road repairs is due to winter traffic than to summer traffic. Much of this larger percentage is directly traceable to the neglect of highways during snow storms.

Under conditions that prevailed years ago the cost of opening snow-bound highways was practically prohibitive. Introduction of snow plows radically changed this condition. A report issued by the State of Connecticut shows that the total cost of snow removal during the winter of 1917, when snowfalls were abnormally heavy, was slightly over $40,00 for a total of 970 miles or about $40 per mile. This state, it may be noted, uses a large number of new snow plows.

Champion Snow Plow attached to a Day-Elder bus opening roads on its route between Providence and East Greenwich Rhode Island.

Snow plow - This snow plow of 19th century design is made entirely of wood and was also known as a plank plow. The wings to the sides were extra wide to carry snow well out over the road edge, leaving a clear smooth track on each side of the cone strip in the centre. The right-hand and left-hand plow were adjustable to a depth independent of sleigh movement.

Snow removal was initially done with hand labour that proved both expensive and scarce. In a council report published in the Goderich Signal of 1895, J. Barker was paid $7 for shovelling snow off the Maitland bridge, Goderich.

Of all the devices offered, the snow plow or grader was the most popular. The horse-drawn grader, particularly one with an offset tongue, proved most effective. The grader pictured here in 1914 also had wheels offset to allow the blade portion to get deeper into the side. It took four horses to draw this grader to clear the streets.

1st Iron Bridge over the Maitland to Saltford, built in 1883

Climax Snow Plows attached to motor buses clear snow from Fifth Avenue in New York City, circa 1920.

Champion Snow Plow – Attached to a Fordson tractor this rear view of the moldboard shows the semicircle shape and tilting adjustment. The automatic blade releasewould allow the cutting edge when it strikes an obstacle, such as a manhole cover or trolley car track, to release the blade and allow it to pass over such obstruction, and then immediately returns to its operating position Note the rollers on the side edges of the mouldboard that are used to guard the blade from hitting the curbs and the street rollers (now called snow plow shoes) would eliminate removal of all the gravel from the street.

Climax Snow Plow – This machine consists of a steel scraper bar attached to a semi-circle and swung under a frame carried by a FWD truck. The side view, bottom, shows wings on the end of the mouldboard to handle the snow to better advantage.

A fleet of F. W. D. trucks with Champion snow plows attached, owned by the Connecticut State Highway Department, are ready for business.

The Economy Snow Remover – The rear view of the Economy snow remover shows the sliding bottom drawn back ready for unloading. The Economy removes snow in somewhat the same way as the wheeled or drag scraper handles dirt. It could pick up loose or heavily packed snow from streets.

In 1917 streets were cleaned in record time with several plows pulled diagonally in unison.

Sidewalk Plows

One of the first all steel sidewalk snow plows

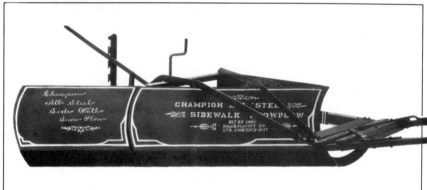

Sidewalk snow plow with extended wing – The rear view of the wing snow plow illustrates how the wing operated by a chain and rod. Often the operator would walk beside the team to keep warm.

Rotary Snowplows

W. L. Stadig of St. Francis, Maine invented the rotary snowplow in 1917.

It was a very ponderous affair about 18 feet in length and of solid steel. It was set upon sleighs, with the machinery working between the bobs. The plow was set immediately behind the front sleigh and raised the snow and fed it back to the rotary cutters which operated on both sides. These cutters would revolve at a high rate, throwing the snow upwards into steel hoods from which the force would send it 40 or 50 feet to the sides of the road. The power generated from a 50 horsepower engine set in the centre top, and with two or four teams hitched to the front of the plow, had no trouble negotiating 7-foot drifts.

Both municipalities and the Ontario government were finding it essential that more attention be paid to the highways, both in construction and in keeping them clear for winter passage.

In 1918 six snow plows were shipped to Outremount, a suburb of Montreal, and eliminated the cost of hiring 300 men for the snow removal work.

A cold task – Snowblowing has never been a pleasurable job, but with the advent of the rotary snowplow the job was done a little quicker. Scenes here show the rotary plow in action in Quebec and Ontario. In 1917 W. L. Stadig came to Goderich to demonstrate his invention, which was being built there. According to an eyewitness account, Mr. Stadig started up the motor and it made quite a roar. The storekeepers came to the doors to see what the racket was all about. Just then the plow started to move ahead, the rotors picked up the snow, and bang went the snow right to the storefronts. One storekeeper had snow in his store before he could close the door, another had a broken window from a stone that the rotors picked up. Mr. Stadig had the snow chute pointed the wrong way. No more demonstrations uptown.

100 Everything for the RoadMaker

Joy Snow Loader

This new loader was on exhibition at the American Road Builders Association Annual Convention and Good Roads Show, in Cleveland, Ohio, in January of 1928. Developed from a successful loading method used by the coal industry, the Joy Snow Loader could load from 10 to 20 cubic yards of snow per minute. It operated on a Hercules Model "G" four cylinder gasoline power unit with 6 speeds forward and 2 speeds reverse.

Adapting the graders — All steel snow plows were mounted on the Power Maintainer for winter work.

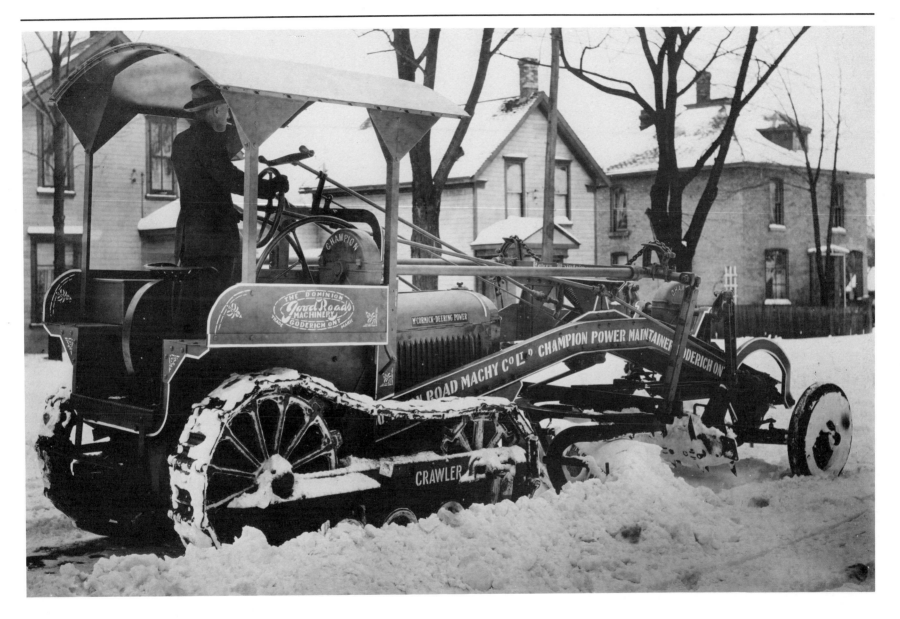

Crawling through the snow – R. G. Johnston tests the first Crawler Tractor Manual Power Grader on a snow-covered street in Goderich using a mouldboard for snow removal.

More improvements – By the late 1930s larger plows were mounted on the graders for increased snow

Champion Snow King - This loading plow was used for widening and clearing when conditions were suitable. It was ideal for airport clearing with a drag or packer towed behind to maintain smooth surfaces for planes to land on. Control is from the tractor cab and the distance, or force, of the discharge is determined by the speed at which the rotor is driven. "The snow when broadcast with the wind just seems to disappear," prospective buyers were told.
Here the Snow King is fitted to a Caterpillar D7 tractor and shown throwing snow with its single auger.

Improved Snow King - By 1939 the Snow King plow was equipped with two ribbed steel rotors with chutes. When widening, full power was delivered to one rotor while the other rotor still revolved to pick up any spilling, thus keeping the roadway thoroughly cleared, as shown below.

Ready for snow clearing – Joe Kerr of Wingham had his truck fitted with a Champion plow and wing in 1940.

The Dominion Road Machinery Company Limited, Goderich, started tooling up for war work in 1941. One of the departments produced large snow rollers for use on airport runways.

Scarifiers

Scarifiers of one kind or another have been used for many years in the work of tearing up worn gravel and stone highways so that they could be resurfaced properly. The best-known type may be briefly described as a heavy frame made of steel, mounted on small wheels, and equipped with picks which are forced into the ground by means of a screw arrangement as shown on these two scarifiers

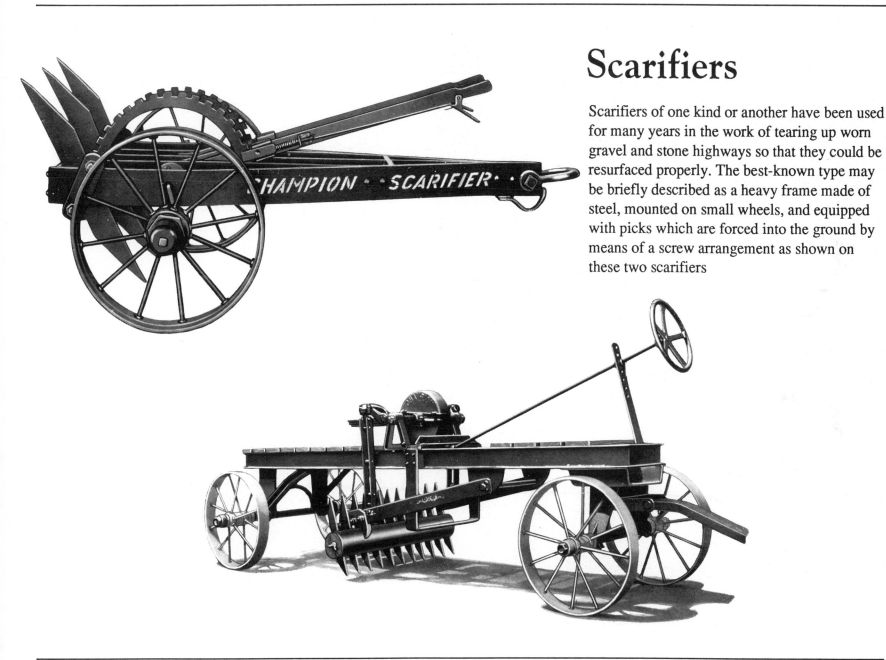

The new model, Killifer scarifier, had teeth mounted onto the frame instead of a separate bar, thus providing a more secure bed for the teeth and more control over the depth of penetration of the ground. It could be pulled by a 45-horsepower tractor and easily turned on the job site.

Street Cleaner and Mud Scraper

The Canada Post, *Lindsay , Ontario, May 11, 1888 – The heavy rainfall of Tuesday night put the streets in the condition desired by Street Inspector Neeman, reducing the mud to a state of liquid stickiness, and Wednesday a large force of men were put to work scraping the streets. It is noticeable that the accumulations are much larger than last year, which may properly be taken to indicate an increasing trade, though it also is evidence of the grinding down of the level of our main street.*

And so the Champion Mud Scraper became an invaluable machine for the rapid and perfect scraping off of mud and dirt from either smooth or uneven surfaces. The feet (or teeth), being flexible with spring attachments, would follow the indentations of the roadway.

Sweepers

With the large-scale use of oil on the roads it became necessary to keep the roads clean and swept to prepare for oil application. There were two designs of horse-drawn sweepers developed in the late 1800s.

The two-horse Champion No. 1-A was simple, yet strong and was nine feet six inches wide with a sweeping width of 7 feet. The power was supplied by a large gear on the drive shaft meshed into the gear on the clutch shaft, which, when the clutch was engaged, carried the power through the chain's sprocket to the broom.

When the fibre became worn at one end, there were driving sprockets at both ends of the broom which allowed for adjustment and prevented uneven wearing of the broom. It was reccommended that the broom fibres be wetted the day before use to get the best results.

Two-wheeled street sweeper (1912) – The one-horse sweeper was developed to meet the demands of municipalities and contractors for use in small towns or for congested or narrow streets in larger cities. The smaller sweeper was only 7 feet 9 inches in width with a sweeping width of 6 feet. The broom was placed at an angle to leave the debris in the curb or gutter.

Champion No. 4 Power Sweeper – Primarily designed in the late 1930s for sweeping and preparing streets and roads for bituminous paving. It was also ideal for removing snow, slush, and leaves, and for levelling sand, chips and gravel. The broom was powered by a 4 cylinder engine and the whole unit could be drawn by a team, tractor, or truck. Its sweeping path was 78 inches. The brush was still made of hickory fibre.

The Champion Steel Reversible Road Roller

The Champion Roller was built of steel with two independent sections with a five-foot face giving a rolling width of five feet, and five feet in diameter. Each roll revolved independently of the other on a steel axle four inches in diameter. All the rollers were built the same size but in four different weights from 2.5 to 5.5 tons.

Early horse-drawn rollers were powered by six or eight horses.

The roller was supplied with two seats, one at either end, and a brake, which would effectively stop the roller on the steepest grade.

The rollers had two steel boxes on top, which would hold about a ton of pig iron or other heavy material, used to increase the weight of the roller when necessary. Picks were added to the rollers to break up the previous road surface so new material could be added

Rollers were fast becoming a necessity as experience showed rolling during road construction was the best way to achieve good roads.

Early Steam Roller

116 Everything for the RoadMaker

While the basic principle remained unchanged, by 1909 the driver operated the controls under the safety of a canopy.

The Steam Roller – The steam roller was first introduced from England in 1869. This Monarch road roller was equipped with a new steam pressured scarifier. An eight-inch steam cylinder equals the power of ten horses.

Monarch Cub Roller – By 1924 rollers were powered by Fordson tractor engines and included such modifications as scarifiers, levellers, and scrapers. Charlie Leach, of Kennett Square, Pennsylvania, became a popular face on many equipment brochures for The American Road Machinery Company. Mr. Leach was an invaluable source of information for this book, drawing upon his vast library of material saved from his many years working for the American firm.

Charlie Leach

Roller designs – Requests from private individuals for rollers had workers busy at the machinery plants. One request in 1936 for a roller was accompanied by an individual bringing in his tractor to be fitted with a grader frame as well as one-ton casting on the rear wheels like the ones used on the graders.

Huron County Roller – This particular model was manufactured by Sandy Construction, Goderich in 1936.

Pressure Distributor

The Monarch Distributor consisted of a steel tank equipped with heating and distributing devices and mounted on a platform spring gear truck. The 600-gallon tank was made of sheet steel and could spread liquid asphalt at a rate of four-tenths of a gallon per square yard.

Pictured below is a distributor tank without a heating unit. The asphalt was heated by an 1874 steam-fire engine. The steam from the engine was channelled through pipes inside the rail tank car that contained the asphalt. When hot enough, it was poured into the tank and distributed by horses. Note the leggings on the horses to protect them from being burned by the tar in this 1930 picture.

Early Liquid Asphalt Distributor – This 1935-1936 distributor was built by Tom Sandy Machine Shop for Huron County road department. Gravel was spread on the road and with a grader the gravel was then put in a windrow on the side of the road. The liquid asphalt was then spread on the road and the gravel levelled. A second coating of liquid asphalt was spread. This was repeated about 6 times and then finally rolled.

122 Everything for the RoadMaker

Rear view – Early liquid asphalt distributors had a hose and spray bar for spray-patching and treating of the roads.

Heating the asphalt – Asphalt materials were heated to not less than 275°F in a Perfection Heating Pan and then transferred to the Distributor for spreading and rolling on the roads.

A mile a day – The Climax Distributor consisted of an air-tight asphalt drum equipped with two sets of distributing valves and nozzles, a heating device to keep the asphalt fluid, an air reservoir, and a Westinghouse air compressor, all mounted on a heavy frame which is in turn supported by four broad rolls and a folding rear bracket. The distributor was designed to be coupled by means of two bars to the draw bar of any steam road roller or traction engine.   It could easily spread one mile of sixteen-foot roadway per day.

Pouring Pots – The Good Roads Pouring Pots were especially valuable on small jobs and for patching work where it was not economical to use a distributing machine. The pots were made of heavy galvanized sheet iron and had an interchangeable spout to provide opening of widths of 1-2 inches to 8-10 inches.

Fort Wayne Distributor – This machine was used for light road preservation and dust-laying work.

Asphalt / Bituminous Plants

When automobiles made their appearance on the macadam roads it quicky became apparent that a better road surface would have to be applied. Investigation showed that the shearing force of rubber-tired wheels driven at a high rate of speed loosened the binding material from the road surface, allowing it to be swept clean by winds and leaving the top course of stone unprotected.

Continued traffic quickly disintegrated the surface and soon ruined the roadway. The dust nuisance became so intolerable with the increased traffic that public health and comfort demanded that remedies be adopted.

The problem was attacked in two ways: one method was to use some substance as a dust palliative without any special regard for road preservation other than that effected by the retention of more dust; the other was to use some type of bituminous material for more durable and easily maintained roads. The principal materials used as palliatives were water, light oils, oil emulsions and light tar compounds, and while it was found that such materials gave fairly good results as dust layers and that they would act to some extent at least as road preservatives, results showed that they did not strike at the root of the trouble. At best their effects were short-lived, and frequent applications, entailing considerable expense, were necessary.

Experiments were made by highway engineers and chemists in all parts of the world, and the solution was found in the bituminous materials. This discovery became almost exclusively used in the building of broken stone roads, in reconstruction work and in laying dust on water bound macadam roads.

The bituminous plants would heat the aggregates to remove the moisture and create a blotter effect when the crude oil was mixed in. This was carefully applied in an even depth over the rolled road surface.

Dust nusiance - Bituminous mixture applied to the roads became the most practical way of eliminating the dust problem.

Stationary Asphalt Plant – The 15th Champion Bituminous Mix Plant was set up in the late 1920s.

Portable Bituminous Plant

The Champion Portable Bituminous Plant 60 was so called because it produced 60 tons of bituminous material in one hour. It consisted of three separate units. The dryer unit, 21 feet long, weighed 6 tons. The combustion unit, 15 feet long, weighed 3 tons, and the mixing unit, 14 feet long, weighed 8 tons. Each unit was mounted on a chassis made of structural steel shapes cross-braced and mounted on solid rubber-tired wheels. The overall length when operating was 40 feet.

From the stock pile, aggregate was loaded into a steel hopper which was so constructed that either pit-run gravel or any predetermined mixture of fine and coarse aggregates that could be obtained would be used. The aggregate was fed to the dryer along a belt conveyor.

Dryer – Interior detail of Champion Dryer, showing the system of flight spiraling scientifically arranged to produce a continuous curtain of aggregate. The dryer's capacity was 60 tons per hour.

Combustion Unit – The oil burner was designed for heavy bunker C-oil. Oil was preheated to 150° F and continually by-passed to a 500-gallon oil storage tank. By virtue of by-passing, the fuel tank was always kept warm. Burner capacity was from 1/4 to 3 gallons per minute. Oil atomized with air preheated to 80° F above atmospheric temperature. The heat exchanger was heated with steam or exhaust gases. The interior of the combustion chamber was lined with fire brick.

The mixing unit consisted of an enclosed elevator and a covered bin. An apron feeder acted as the bin bottom. By keeping the speed constant the amount of aggregate could be determined accurately by two adjustable gates.

The aggregate was first heated to an excess of 212° F and then sprayed with bitumen by three spray nozzles operating at a pressure of 50 pounds per square inch.

The sprayed aggregate fell into a double pug mill consisting of two parallel rows of mixing arms, each eight feet long rotating in opposite directions. The mixing time was one minute, after which the material was elevated to a steel bottom-dump jack-leg bin.

A mammoth machine – One of the largest dryers in Canada was manufactured in Goderich and its shipment was reported in the weekly paper, the Goderich Signal Star 1937:
" Last week a 16-ton piece of machinery manufactured at the plant of the Dominion Road Machinery Company was shipped by rail to Quebec. The machine, a dryer unit for work on bituminous roads, was built at a cost of $11,000 for the Provincial Construction Company. Not only is this machine the largest single piece ever put out by the local firm, it is also the largest of its kind in Canada. With a 40-foot chassis the machine is composed of a huge cylinder 24 feet in length and six feet in diameter. It will turn out 100 tons of evenly dried and heated gravel in one hour. It was just one month in the making. It was a major feat of engineering to load this behemoth on a flat car at the CNR yards, an auxiliary from Stratford being used."

132 Everything for the RoadMaker

The Surveyors

In 1920, C. F. Aylsworth, O.L.S., addressed the Association of Ontario Land Surveyors with the following words: "Many years ago, members of this Association were among the first to expound the doctrines of scientifically constructed roads, or what were then, and now known as, 'good roads'.

Normally these two surveyors would be 100 to 200 feet apart and a little less well-dressed. The man on the left is setting out a line with a theodolite, while the man on the right has a range pole.

Surveying, the marriage of the science of measuring with the art of law, was a vital first step in setting out a road. Each particular job, at that time, usually consisted of establishing on the ground the centre line and legal boundaries of the road, possibly taking elevations and noting topographic features and soils. The general concept was to help open up a 'good road'.

It is interesting to note that 'good roads' was first a description, then a concept, a concept which sometime later became the formal name of a company.

The following pictures show survey crews on the job during the period of 1900 to 1920.

Surveyors lived a very simple life on the trail, one which included doing their own laundry.

The best time to establish lines in rugged areas was in the spring, before swamps and bogs thawed. Note the 'theodolite', or transit, on the ground in front of the gentleman in buckskins.

134 Everything for the RoadMaker

Survey crews included additional men for tree-cuttting. Equipment and supplies were carted by pack-horse into the area to be surveyed.

This surveyor took advantage of more up-to-date technology and left his pack horse behind. Note the surveyor's range pole strapped to the side of the automobile.

Road Crews

A quick photo for history – In 1926 the Wardsville road crew took a break for this photo. Operators of the heavy steam equipment had to have a licence.

The hot asphalt was spread by hand with rakes and later rolled with a steam roller, as shown below.

Road crew under the Statute of Labour in 1907 in Goderich Township, Huron County

Wardsville crew – Spreading hot asphalt by hand and rolling with a steam roller.

Blasting a new highway —Road crews were responsible for a large number of jobs. This crew is loading dynamite into drilled holes in the rock bed. The Dufferin Construction Company of Toronto working for the Provincial Highways department, were constructing the Dundas Road in Nelson Township in 1921.

138 Everything for the RoadMaker

An old idea still at work – The basics of road building start with clearing the area. Crawler vehicles were not widely accepted until after world War I. This Cletrac is pulling a two-wheel road drag to clear top soil out of the road bed. The road drag has not changed since it was first developed in the 1800s.

Preparing for a cement road – Road crews prepared the forms, right, and levelled the surface by manual shovelling. Behind them is the steam-driven cement mixer.

Photo courtesy of the Ministry of Transportation No. 18200

Cement roads – Horse-drawn carts would unload the gravel into a bucket which would then be elevated to the mouth of the steam driven cement mixer. Once mixed the cement would be poured into a bucket at the back, which was attached to a boom enabling the load to be deposited in a swath across the width of the road. Photo courtesy of the Ministry of Transportation No. 18265

Basic principles of road building – Keeping water off roadways is a basic principle of good road making. Worn-out gravel roads were rebuilt regularly to bring up the crown and allow water to run off. Photo courtesy of the Ministry of Transportation No. 18276

Parade of road builders – Building roads was a massive job. Parades of men and equipment moved along, rolling, smoothing, and leaving asphalt surfaces for the public to travel on more easily.

Manual turntables (1920) were used to get loads of gravel rerouted to different locations along the newly built roads.

Photos courtesy of the Ministry of Transportation No. 18275 and No S 17546

Road rolling in 1918 – A steam roller kept this road crew busy preparing the road and sloping up the shoulders.
Photo courtesy of Ministry of Transportation No. 18330

144 Everything for the RoadMaker

Sanitary Engineer – Armed with a scavenger cart, young men would pick up debris along the streets. The cart featured a swivel wheel at back, large 30 inch wheels, and a heavy galvanized iron can. The complete outfit sold for $18.25 in 1922.

Champion Road Building Sprinkler – Equipped with a hand pump for loading, this sprinkler had a capacity of 300 to 500 gallons.

Water sources – Operators of street sprinklers sought out rivers and creeks for water when water hydrants were not available. This motor truck, circa1920, had a gravity sprinkler attachment driven by the truck motor. The pump would draw water up 25 feet at the rate of 250 to 300 gallons per minute, which proved to be a very valuable feature.

The horse-drawn sprinkler is being filled with the aid of a hydrant.

Sprinklers were important for many road surfaces. The bottom photo shows the sprinkler with both valves working independently of each other on a dusty gravel street. The width of spray and quantity of water were controlled by the driver.

An improvement on the Power Flushing Machine or sprinkler was the addition of a sprinkler on the front. The top photo shows how effective the Power Flusher cleaned brick or cobblestone streets, an important sanitary feature.

Etnyre Motor Truck Flushing Machine – This model operated with 50 pounds of pressure obtained through a centrifugal pump connected directly to the truck motor. The flushing nozzle could be turned to any angle to meet various conditions. Note the cobblestone road.

Wagons

Michigan Wagons were among the first dump wagons and proved invaluable when putting gravel on the roads. You can see the small drop seats for the workmen located along the side of the box. One crew would ride with the wagon and load and unload it at the sites, saving the cost of having a second crew waiting at the other end of the job.

Champion Dump Wagon – This wagon could be economically used in hauling material such as stone, gravel, brick, sand, coal, lime, etc. Special attention was paid to the draught to enable the horses to draw the load with a minimum of power.

One of the first ways of applying gravel was with a unique bottomed wagon. The wagon operator would turn the round handles on the back of the wagon causing the bottom boards to turn sideways allowing the gravel to be spread onto the road as the wagon was driven forward.

Epilogue

1946: The grader continued to be refined with overall improvement in the general appearance, plus major changes in cab design and improved operator comfort.

1948: Dramatic changes in the frame introduced Champion's high-arch design. The power was greatly increased, and improvments were made in the front end geometry and blade lift system.

1958: Further developments in cab design and frame geometry were introduced, and the hydraulics were further redefined. Champion's patented "power-plus" circle turn system replaced conventional circle motor with twin hydraulic cylinders.

1964: Further design improvements were made as the grader of today took shape. New frame geometry was introduced and changes were made to the engine and power-train.

1975: Champion's 700 Series was launched with a whole new generation of grader technology with design improvements in every component. A wide range of models and options was offered.

Champion Today

Road makers of today are still building roads, and look for bigger and better equipment. To the present day, Champion Road Machinery Limited has continued to be a Canadian success story. From February, 1910, the company has remained in Goderich, and since 1943 has been on Maitland Road. As well, Champion built additional buildings in the Goderich Industrial Park in the 1970s to accommodate their expanding operations.

In 1988, Champion was sold to management and a group of investors led by Sequioa Associates of California. The company remains Canadian, however, and it has thrived. New capital has been invested in plant and buildings, and the relationship between company and community continues to prosper. Champion commands an ever growing share of the worldwide grader market. Through the years, Champion has continued to focus on road building equipment. In the late 1950s the Motor Grader became the sole focus of the company's operations. From then until the present day the company has built its reputation on this unique product and various attachments for it. Today's Champions have been sold in 95 countries around the world, in markets as diverse as Alaska to Antarctica, Zimbabwe to Japan.

The product that Champion produces today is called Series III. It is the third generation of graders in the highly successful 700 Series, which was first produced in 1975. There are six basic model sizes., available with either rigid or articulated frames, plus one variable horsepower and three all-wheel-drive models. Champion continues to make a wide variety of grader attachments, including rippers, scarifiers, and snowplows.

By focusing on just one product, Champion Road Machinery Limited has proven itself a strong player on the world construction equipment stage, and will continue to do so in the 1990s and beyond.

1984: When the company's second century began Champion was building the second generation 700 Series, the standardized Series II grader, with a superior operator's environment, a state-of-the-art transmission, and the highest productivity in the industry.

1989: Today's Series III grader was designed by listening to the needs of customers around the world. Added to the great features of Series II were a more efficient circle, simplified hydraulics, and improved service access and rearward visibility.

Acknowledgements

I would like to acknowledge and thank the following people and organizations for their help and support during the years I spent researching and writing this book. It was both a pleasure and an adventure to see what many people had tucked away, and saved for so many years, and were so generous in offering to me. Special thanks to Mr. and Mrs. Charles Leach without whom I would never have been able to do the book. My family was especially supportive to the point were my daughter thought she was going to go blind from typing fine printed photo copies of old newspapers. It has been a real treasure hunt.

Mr. & Mrs. Charles Leach, Kennett Square Pennsylvania
Gloria L. Currence, Kennett Square Pennsylvania
Goderich Library Branch staff –
  Marg Bushell, Elaine Blair, Karen Blackwell
  and Reg Thompson

Champion Road Machinery Limited
  Robin Sully
  Mickey Giesbriecht, Graham MacDonald, Rita Ross, Laverine Culbert, Bob Allen, Graham McEwan, Ken Mullen, Sid Lawson, Vince Young, Mary Hussey MacLaren, L. B. (Bucky) Graham, Stan Whiteman, Barry Page, Sam Anderson, Barb Shewfelt, Ken Hunter, Fred Sandy, Jackie Rahbek, Betty Johnston Elliott, Eric Johnston, Randall Marriott, Jim Harvey, Larry Mohring, Ron Pennington, Ken McGee, Ron Patterson, Peter Patterson, Ray Barker, Ron Barker, Susan Barlow Jeffrey, Bob Barlow, E.D. Entyre & Co., Oregon, Illinois
National Archives of Canada
Archives of Ontario
Saskatchewan Archives Board
Ontario Agricultural Museum, Milton, Ontario
Huron County Pioneer Museum, Goderich, Ontario

American Road Machine Company trade show in Goderich, 1913.

Acknowledgements

Allan McGillivray, curator of the Uxbridge-Scott Museum, Uxbridge
Uxbridge-Scott Historical Society, Uxbridge, Ontario
Staff of the Huron County Land Registry Office
Don Rivers and Allen Findlay
Doug Culbert
Rockville Museum, Rockville, Indiana
Proofreaders – Lisa Gunby, Reg Thompson
Photograph of Goderich courtesy of Mac Campbell Photography
Special thanks to the Ontario Ministry of Transportation for photos and for permission to use 'Footpaths to Freeways'

The last toll gate in Ontario, located at Sarnia and Forence Road, 1926. Photo credit Ministry of Transportation 18332

NOV 1 1980

Date Due

DISCARD

4927

791.437   Allen, Robert Thomas.
Vio   The violin; from the story by George
         Pastic and Andrew Welsh. Photography
         by George Pastic. Featuring Maurice
         Solway as the old man. Toronto,
         McGraw-Hill Ryerson, 1976.
             78 p. illus., music.

             1. The Violin (Motion picture)
         I. Pastic, George. II. Welsh, Andrew.
         III. Title.
         0070823006   0017647 6/EX

THE VIOLIN

THE VIOLIN

From the story by George Pastic and Andrew Welsh

text by
Robert Thomas Allen

photography by
George Pastic

Featuring Maurice Solway as the old man

McGraw-Hill Ryerson Limited

Toronto   Montreal   New York
London   Sydney   Johannesburg
Mexico   Panama   Düsseldorf   Kuala Lumpur
São Paulo   New Delhi   Auckland

THE VIOLIN

Copyright © McGraw-Hill Ryerson Limited, 1976.
Story by Andrew Welsh and George Pastic, from the film *The Violin* produced by Sincinkin Limited.
ISBN 0-07-082300-6
1 2 3 4 5 6 7 8 9 0 BP 5 4 3 2 1 0 9 8 7 6
Printed and bound in Canada

his story happened not very long ago on an island. It wasn't an island far out in the sea. It was an island in the harbour of a big city. Yet it was a real island, quiet and peaceful. In the winter cottontail rabbits hopped across the frozen lagoons.

Chris and Danny lived on the island all winter. They were great friends and played together in the snow and had a secret hiding place.

5

It was the hollow of a big willow tree.

Chris, the older boy, who was often quiet and thoughtful, had been saving his money for a long time. He knew that now there should be enough to buy the wonderful thing that he had been longing to have.

On this special morning Chris reached into the tree and felt around.

"Is it there?" Danny asked.

Chris took a jar full of coins from the tree. He held it up and jingled it and dropped a few more coins into the jar. There was enough! Anyway the boys thought there was enough.

The two boys began to shout. They danced in the snow, and ran from the woods — through an old garden of an empty cottage, down the path to the docks, over the gangplank onto the ferryboat that was smoking and puffing ready to take islanders across the bay to the city.

9

The boom of the ferryboat's horn sounded as if it were telling the very clouds that something important was going to happen this day.

By this time, as he often did, Danny looked as if he were coming apart. His mother sometimes pinned his mitts to his coat, looking him in the eye saying, "Now don't lose these, Danny," but he usually lost them anyway.

Chris stood at the rail as the boat moved across the water. He looked serious now that his dream was soon to come true. Danny asked, "How do you know you can play it when you get it, Chris?"

"I know I can," Chris said.

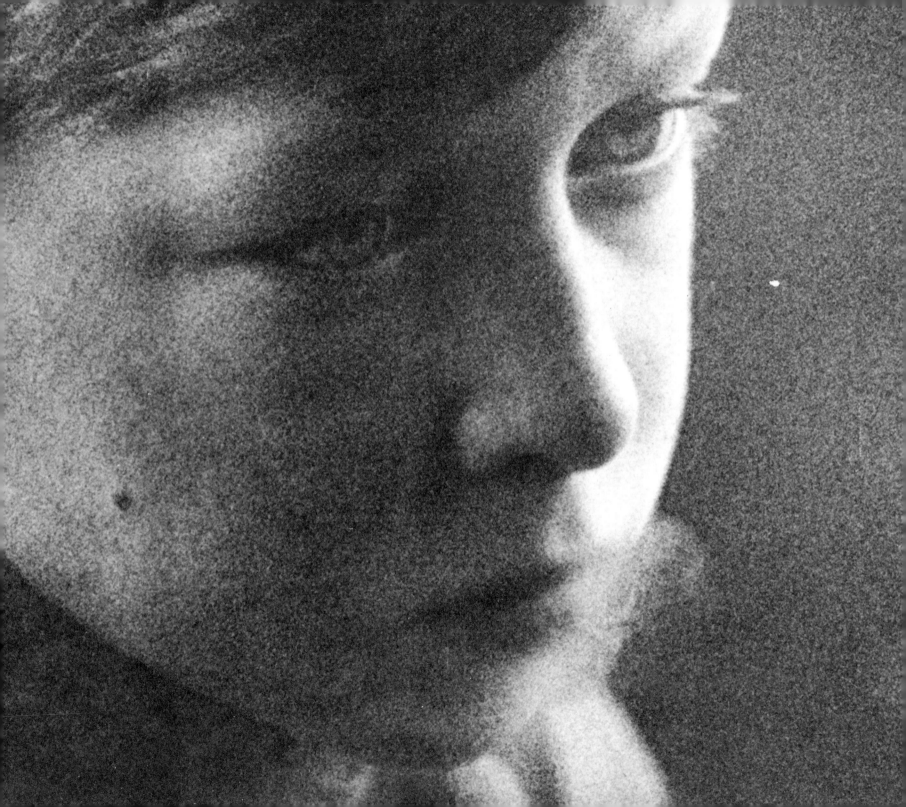

The people on the busy streets hurried along looking straight ahead as if there were nothing special in the store windows. But the window the boys finally reached and gazed into was a magic world, like a stage. The winter sun shone on a patch of faded blue cloth. An orange cat was asleep in the corner and there in the middle was the magic object that Chris had wanted for such a long time, graceful and shiny as a new chestnut —

a violin.

It looked so beautiful that Chris stood for a moment outside the door to the store, hardly able to believe that soon it would be his own.

When he opened the door, a man looked up from behind the counter. Chris handed him the jar of coins to pay for the violin — the one in the window. But life is full of disappointments, and grown-ups sometimes make things worse with awful jokes.

"Oho! So you want to buy an expensive violin with a jar full of pennies and dimes?" The man looked at the jar of coins as if he didn't think very much of it. "By the time you save enough nickels for *that* violin you'll have a long grey beard."

Chris just stared. But Danny was anxious to help. He told the man that he could have other things besides the money and began taking his prized possessions from his pockets — pictures of birds, a shiny alley, a hawk's foot. The man looked at them as if nothing in life would ever interest him again.

"Chicken's feet I don't need," he said.

"It's a hawk's foot."

"I don't need hawks' feet either. With hawks' feet I can't pay the rent."

Sometimes, though, people aren't as mean as they first seem. When the boys started to leave, the man called to them, "Just a minute now. There was one — let me think." He shifted some things around on a bottom shelf and held up another violin so Chris could see it. "Here. This one has everything the other one has — strings, a bow, a place to put your chin. It's a better one for a boy. I can let you have it for the money in the jar."

On the way home on the ferry, holding the violin, Chris felt somehow that the world had changed. He couldn't believe that the violin the man had sold him was as good as the one he had seen at first. Nothing would cheer him up, not even looking at Danny. Chris had dreamt of owning and playing a violin ever since one day he went with his mother to a concert. He never forgot how he felt when a boy no older than he was came out and played a violin. Beautiful sounds seemed to fall from the air inside the concert hall.

When they were back home, Chris took the violin from the case and put it under his chin. He could almost hear the hush of a huge audience waiting for him to play. He drew the bow across the strings. But the sound that came from the violin was nothing like the music in Chris's head. It was like a squeaking door, or perhaps a growling pup.

Danny went outside and put his hands over his ears. Soon afterwards, Chris came out of the cottage and sat down beside Danny on the step.

"This violin is no good," he said. He put the violin in its case and walked away from the cottage. Danny followed him.

24

When he came to a wire wastebasket, he dropped the violin in among the old newspapers. He felt better, but not much. It was snowing and he began to make a snowball to throw at Danny but he noticed that Danny was watching something in the distance.

A man was coming along the path — a strange-looking man, wearing a black coat and a kind of high black hat Chris had never seen before. As he moved through the snow his coat flapped and he looked like a big crow that had decided to walk instead of fly. Chris and Danny watched him sit down on the park bench; then the man looked into the basket and lifted out the violin.

29

He opened the case and took out the violin. The way he tightened the bow and tuned the strings and put the violin under his chin, like something he was trying to warm up, you could tell he was used to violins.

"But the man has not heard *that* violin!" Chris whispered to Danny, "I wonder what he'll do when he hears the awful sound it makes?"

But when the man began to play, with the snow falling around him, Chris knew that he had never heard such beautiful music. The boys came right up behind the bench where the man was playing, but he was so lost in his music that he didn't notice them. Chris knew now that it wasn't the fault of the violin when it made terrible sounds; it just needed someone who knew how to play it. He wanted his violin back.

"I didn't really throw it away," Chris whispered to Danny, "I just put it there for a while." Which shows you how easy it is to believe anything you want to believe, even when it isn't true.

The man put the violin back in its case and started to walk away with it. Chris and Danny followed him. What would the man do, Chris wondered, when he asked for the violin back? Would the man turn around and yell or maybe even take a swing at them with the violin case?

Danny never seemed to worry about things like that and when they caught up with the man, Danny just tugged his sleeve and said, "That's our violin."

Chris began to tell the man why the violin was in the wastebasket. The man peered at him over his glasses and smiled, and seemed so glad of their company, that Chris knew he would give him not only the violin but almost anything. The man told them where his cottage was.

"I'll take the violin home with me," he said. "I'll polish it and tune it. If you tell your mothers where you're going, you can come over and get it."

The old man's cottage was the most wonderful place. It had the same look that Chris liked about Danny — nice and friendly but falling apart. Magazines and books had fallen off shelves. There were piles of sheet music where there should have been cups and plates and there were cups and plates on top of sheet music. There was a pet rabbit on the table and a pigeon in a cage. Things fell from strange places if you jiggled anything. "Never mind picking them up," the man would say. A pink umbrella fell off a bookcase.

"Don't bother picking it up," the man said. "I found that. I use it as a sunshade when I go out in my rowboat."

You could have lost Danny among the things that the man hadn't put away in their proper place. Chris asked the man if he'd play the violin for him again. This time the man played a different tune — light and fast and kind of funny.

He played to the pigeon. He played to the rabbit. He played to Chris and Danny. It looked so easy that Chris wanted to try again, but he made such a squawking sound that Danny put his hands over his ears and went outside.

Chris knew now that he *did* want to learn to play the violin after all. The man showed him how the violin was made, and told him something of its special place among instruments. A violinist can make almost as many sounds with a violin as a singer can with the human voice, playing notes that are very low and very high, making music sad or soft, light, gentle, bright, or strong.

Violins, the man said, were first made over four hundred years ago in the small town of Cremona in northern Italy. One maker was Antonius Stradivarius, who made the finest violins of his time.

The man showed Chris how to hold the violin and how to draw the bow across the strings. When he did it, he made a wonderful, sweet sound. When Chris tried, he made a sound like wood splitting, but before he left the man told him to come back and he would teach him how to play.

uring the following months when he gave Chris lessons, he sometimes looked off into space, as if his thoughts were thousands of miles away. He'd say "I remember one time..." and tell of something that happened long ago. Gradually Chris formed a picture in his mind of a mountain village and peaks that turned gold in the sun, and of big cities and after-theatre parties, and a bright far-off world where people loved music and talked music and lived for music. Then something had happened that sent the man wandering into strange lands with his violin.

The snow began to thaw, and by the time the lake had turned pale blue and the willows looked like green fountains, the man seemed pleased with his pupil. On warm days he and Chris played duets sitting on the rocks by the shore of the lake.

The man talked more and more often now of the mountains he had known as a boy and he was sometimes far away in his thoughts. Once when Chris told him he'd never want to be without his violin — the one he once threw away — the man looked at him a long time and then said, "We sometimes become too attached to things." He looked down at his own violin. "This is like an old friend to me, but if I had to part with it, I wouldn't stop loving music."

Chris thought it a strange thing to say, but then forgot about it because he and Danny and the man were having so much fun together. They took rides on the ferryboat and went on picnics. Sometimes the man lay in the grass just looking up at the blue sky, listening to Chris play his violin.

They went to the zoo where Danny ran around as if he knew each of the animals personally. Chris saw the animals as if they were not in the zoo at all: the camels in long dusty caravans moving across the desert, the deer in a northern forest, the fox crossing a dewy meadow at dawn when the woods seem to float on a morning mist.

Chris knew his violin like a friendly face. He knew there was a chip out of one of the pegs which tighten the strings and a little dark swirl in the grain of the wood seemed to watch him like a friendly eye as he played.

Yet in a strange way, when he played down by the wooden bridge in the soft sunlight of late summer, he felt a bit sad. The lonely rustle of the cottonwood trees, or the way a leaf fell beside him, like a tear, seemed to tell him that a time comes when friends must part.

One day Chris and Danny were on the bridge. Chris had his violin. Danny was fishing — his kind of fishing — catching minnows in a net tied to the end of a line, so that he could put them in a jar of water and look at them. Just as Chris started to play his favorite piece, Danny called out, "It's stuck!" He was tugging on his fishing line.

"Wait a minute," Chris said, "I'll help you." He put his violin down and went to help. But Danny didn't want help even from Chris. "Leave it alone!"

Chris caught hold of the pole. Danny butted him with his head.

"Stop it. Stop it!" Chris said. Grabbing Danny, he fell backward, laughing.

There was an awful cracking sound.

Chris took the violin from the case. It was a terrible sight: crushed and splintered, its strings limp like the wrappings of an open parcel. For Chris it was as if a cloud had passed over the sun. Danny was talking anxiously beside him, saying, "I'll fix it, Chris, I'll nail it together. I'll glue it together. I'll buy you a new one."

"I'll never play a violin again," Chris said, and wouldn't say any more.

Chris leaned against the railing of the bridge. His stomach felt sore with sadness. He didn't even look up when he heard Danny racing down the steps. He didn't know, or care, that Danny was racing off to find the man and tell him about the accident. Danny was sure the man would know what to do to help.

When he got to the man's cottage Danny found a note on the door. He could read a few words. He read "Dear Boys" and he knew the man had written it for them and that he wasn't there. Where had he gone?

Danny knew the man often went for a walk along the lakeshore. He pulled the note off the door and ran towards the lake as fast as he could.

When Danny found the man he said all in one breath, "I broke the violin. I mean Chris broke it, but I shoved him. He's sitting on the bridge. He said he'd never play again."

At first the man looked at him sadly as if he didn't hear. He spoke as if to himself "Chris mustn't say that." Then he said, "Wait here for a minute, Danny. I'd like to talk to Chris alone," and began to walk anxiously toward the bridge.

Danny felt sure the man would know what to do. But sometimes grown-ups aren't sure what to do. Walking towards the bridge, the man knew he had to make a difficult decision. He had owned his violin for a long, long time. But it wasn't because it was a very special violin that the decision was so hard to make. It was because he wasn't sure that his decision would help Chris. A gift for music is only a beginning. It takes years of hard work to become a musician. But he could think of nothing else to do; the man went up the steps.

Chris looked up and saw the man standing in front of him in his strange coat and hat, his face kind of sagging with worry. "Danny told me what happened," the man said. He held his own violin out to Chris. "This is yours now. I can get another — some day. But only you know whether you will go on and practice and work hard to become a fine musician."

Chris just shook his head. His throat felt tight. He couldn't speak. He never wanted to play a violin again — any violin. The feeling of knowing that he could play had come to an end.

The man went down the steps and stood for a long time on the path, looking very thoughtful. Then he put his violin on the bottom step, picked up the pigeon cage and his other things and walked slowly away.

Chris just sat there. The man had been gone a few minutes when Danny raced up the bridge calling, "Chris! Chris!" He handed the letter to Chris. "I found this nailed to his door. He's gone. The pigeon is gone. The rabbit is gone. We may never see him again."

Chris ran down off the bridge. Danny started after him, then turned and picked up the violin the man had left for Chris. He caught up with Chris as he ran through the woods.

66

"Where will he be?" Danny asked.

"I don't know."

They reached the old willow tree where they once hid their jar of coins, long ago last winter.

Chris climbed up into the branches and looked around.

"I see him! Over there. In his boat. He's rowing out from shore."

They raced down a path through the woods and faded gardens and along a boardwalk. They reached the rocks on the shore where Chris and the man had played their duets. The man was out on the lake in his boat, rowing with the pink umbrella shading the pigeon and rabbit. He was too far out to hear the boys' shouts, or perhaps too far away in his thoughts.

Then Chris felt Danny nudge him with the violin. Chris knew what Danny meant. Perhaps music would be the only thing the man could hear. He thought of his own old violin lying broken on the bridge. He had never played another violin and was afraid he would make the same squawking sounds on this violin that he made when he first tried to play his own. Yet the violin felt just right under his chin. He began to play a tune the man had taught him.

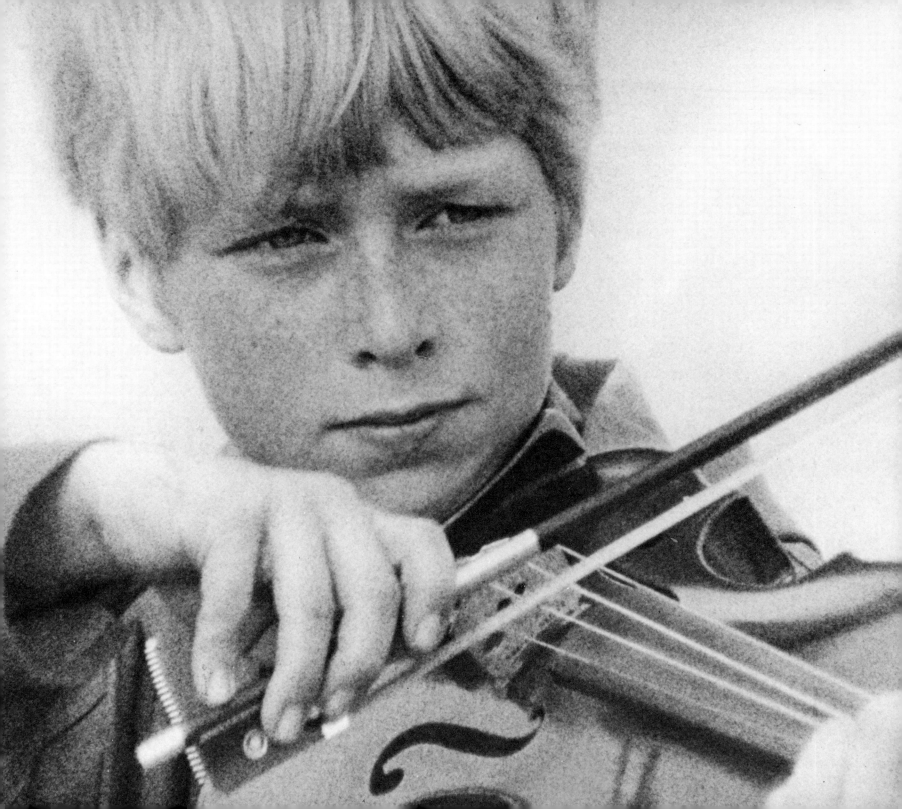

As Chris played, he felt as though the man were beside him once again. The music soared out over the blue water, as light and graceful as a seagull gliding on a summer breeze.

"He hears you!" shouted Danny.

Danny was crying, "We won't ever see him again."
Chris pretended he didn't hear Danny.

Later he'd tell him that nobody ever says goodbye who leaves the world beautiful music.